Indian
Aircraft
Industry

Indian Aircraft Industry

Air Commodore
Jasjit Singh
AVSM, VrC, VM (Retd)

KW Publishers Pvt Ltd
New Delhi

in association with

Centre for Air Power Studies
New Delhi

The **Centre for Air Power Studies** is an independent, non-profit, academic research institution established in 2002 under a registered Trust to undertake and promote policy-related research, study and discussion on the trends and developments in defence and military issues, especially air power and the aerospace arena, for civil and military purposes. Its publications seek to expand and deepen the understanding of defence, military power, air power and aerospace issues without necessarily reflecting the views of any institution or individuals except those of the authors.

Jasjit Singh
Director
Centre for Air Power Studies
P-284, Arjan Path
Subroto Park
New Delhi 110010

Tele: (91-11) 25699131
E-mail: diroffice@aerospaceindia.org

KNOWLEDGE WORLD

Published in India by
Kalpana Shukla
KW Publishers Pvt Ltd
4676/21, First Floor, Ansari Road, Daryaganj, New Delhi 110002
T: +91.11.23263498 / 43528107 E: mail@kwpub.in / knowledgeworld@vsnl.net

ISBN: 978-93-80502-51-9

Printed at Aegean Offset Printers, Greater NOIDA

CONTENTS

Dedicated to

Hindustan Aeronautics Ltd

and its

magnificent men and machines

on its 70th Anniversary

Preface

If God wanted Man to fly, He would have given him wings
— Anonymous

Hence, we need aeroplanes; and they have to be conceptualised to identify their task, the design work to shape a machine that would fulfil those tasks and roles, and a production agency that would manufacture it to the specifications laid down. Only then would Man get his wings to fly. Even a preliminary look at this sentence would show that these tasks must be seamlessly meshed if Man is to fly and 'touch the sky with glory.'

The aircraft industry in India, now seventy years old, like the country itself, is full of paradoxes. There exists one view that the industry has performed marvellously, and a string of statistics is trotted out for the numbers of aircraft and aero-engines manufactured and overhauled. Even without these statistics, it is clear that Hindustan Aeronautics Limited (HAL), the main and so far the only agency that manufactures aircraft, has an enormous infrastructure and capabilities. Its scientists, engineers and designers are of a recognised high quality and have worked hard and long in trying to create self-reliance in the country. There is another view that it has failed to create the requisite capability in design and development and, hence, the pattern that evolved since the late 1960s was that of new types of aircraft either being purchased from abroad or foreign designed aircraft being produced under licence in India. It is sad to see that there was a clear three decades gap between the design and development of the first indigenously designed combat aircraft (in 1956) and the second attempt (in the late 1980s); and during these three decades, aviation technology had advanced exponentially. In between, HAL did undertake upgrades of aircraft like the Gnat to the Ajeet but that proved counter-productive. Meanwhile, at the end of the design life of every aircraft, the country has been looking at buying a replacement either directly or under licence from abroad.

But before we start identifying where we have gone right or wrong, we need to recognise the background – the starting point so to say and the base-line of the national industrial capacity and aviation industry in 1947. To understand that, we have to recognise that for long and certainly till the mid-18th century, India's share in global manufacturing was almost a quarter of what the world produced; it was second only to China which produced around one-third of the global output. This was the reason that the British, French, Portugese and others came to India to trade and then progressively Britain expanded its control over India and its material and manpower resources. Till 1858, in fact, India was ruled by the East India Company which had only a charter to trade in India. It was only after the Great Mutiny of 1857-58 that the Crown took over the Government in India. One major consequence of this process was that from the mid-18th century, the Indian (and Chinese) share in global manufacture dropped by 1950 to just a fraction of the total and the United States, UK and other European powers took the place of China and India. The reasons are not far to seek. By the mid 18th century, the Industrial Revolution had started, actually centred on Britain and its utilisation of coal to run engines on steam. It also led to industrialisation of war and technological advances in the instruments of war. The imbalance in the technology of arms facilitated the progressive expansion of British rule over India. A similar process was going on in other colonies under the European empires of yesteryears, which after decolonisation were called the "Third World," in fact, the developing and underdeveloped countries of the world. If they (and India) had not been brought under European empires, perhaps they might have been able to access the roots of science and technology which caused the Industrial Revolution, even if slower than Western Europe and North America had.

But the way history moved was different. The colonisation of India rapidly began to deindustrialise the country and it became the primary exporter of raw material to Britain, while manufactured goods from Britain were exported to India. Even the two World Wars hardly added to India's industrial capacity, and the British made maximum use of Indian labour for plantations abroad and its soldiers for its wars from Africa to China. The Afro-Asian world is dotted with cemeteries and memorials to Indian soldiers (over 4,000 were cremated in Iran over four decades in the early half of the 20th century). Against this background, it would have been naïve to expect that India would be a storehouse of defence industry and technology by the end of World War II. And that is exactly what the facts of history reveal. In fact, there was even an ongoing rivalry between the United States and Great Britain during World War II in regard to not only the future of India, but the emerging influence of American weapons and equipment.

It needs to be recalled that the first aircraft industry in India was set up as a private joint venture between an American entrepreneur and an Indian industrialist, with the Maharaja of Mysore strongly supporting it by giving land in Bangalore and investing in 50 percent of the shares in the new company, Hindustan Aircraft Private Ltd. But it was soon taken over by the British government in New Delhi and leased to the US Army

Air Force (USAAF) for overhaul and repair work at the cost of design and development of future aircraft. This was soon backed up by the inimitable J.R.D. Tata who set up an aircraft factory in Pune to manufacture one of the best British fast fighter-bombers, the de Havilland Mosquito in 1942, which New Delhi soon ordered to be closed down. Tata was to regretfully state:[1]

> *I think it was purely that they (the British) didn't want India to make a good aeroplane to compete with the British, so they killed it.* Had we started with the Mosquito, we would have gone on to other aeroplanes. (Emphasis added.)

It is in this background that independent India had to formulate its defence policies and industry. Prime Minister Nehru strongly believed in building heavy industry as the foundation of India's industrialisation, and in retrospect, he was right. But he gave a strong push and support to indigenisation of defence industry, since he believed that no country is truly independent unless it is independent in the matters of armaments. Although there is no specific paper outlining the strategy at a time when the country had no capital, no market, no major industry, very little technical scientific resources, rampant poverty and faced a war within weeks of independence, the events as they unfolded, often with Nehru's direct intervention, provide us with a crucial sense of the strategy adopted. In summary, a high priority was accorded to achieving self-reliance in defence (and, hence, aircraft) industry. And aircraft started to be acquired with a three-strand strategy: (i) by direct purchase; (ii) through licensed production; and (iii) by initiating indigenous design

---

1. Alka Sen, *Glimpses into Indian Aviation 1910-1997* (Bombay: Indian Aviation News Services Ltd., 1998), p. 435.

and development. All three strands moved ahead in parallel paths during the Nehru era.

During the 15 years before the Sino-Indian War in 1962, HAL moved ahead rapidly; it designed a number of light aircraft including the basic trainer, the HT-2, began the design of the jet trainer Kiran, and manufactured the Vampire fighter under licence. It undertook most of the development of the British designed Gnat light fighter – the famous Gnat fighter which acquired the reputation of "Sabre Killer" in the 1965 War with Pakistan. Above all, it started an ambitious project in 1956 to manufacture a multi-role combat aircraft, the HF-24 Marut which turned out to be an outstanding design. Notwithstanding our inability to get an adequately powerful engine for it, three squadrons equipped with the aircraft served the country well in the 1971 War on the western front. In the design of the HF-24, the basic tenet of the aircraft industry that aircraft are designed around known, reliable and operational engines, was ignored by South Block and even adequate steps were not taken to accept the not so costly offer of the Bristol engine designers to complete the development of the Bristol Orpheus 12 at a cost of then GBP 3 million which equalled the cost of 3-4 airframes at that time

As noted above, during the Nehru era, the aircraft industry rested on three strands of self-reliance: indigenous design and development, licensed manufacture, and outright import in some cases. Unfortunately, after the 1962 War, the need for expansion of the Indian Air Force (IAF) led to rapidly increased demands of modern aircraft of all types since the IAF force level was authorised by the Cabinet to be increased from the earlier sanction of 33 squadrons to a 64-squadron force (with 50 combat squadrons), and the country's defence needs were mostly met by licensed production of hundreds of fighter and transport aircraft besides helicopters, although the force level was still curtailed to an interim level of 45 squadrons due to shortage of aircraft. The trouble is that we seem to have become complacent (or incapable of professional thinking). In the process, the three-strand self-reliance model shrank to just two strands, with indigenous design and development relegated to inactivity. But it was the third strand, which is the most crucial element in creating autonomy in aircraft and other industrial enterprises, that suffered a serious setback, amounting to neglect, for more than three decades. HAL's design bureau in the Bangalore Division was virtually emasculated.

When the IAF asked for a combat aircraft in the early 1980s, the Light Combat Aircraft (LCA), which was also meant to be a low cost aircraft, this finally led to a situation where an ad-hoc design bureau was created as the Aeronautical Development Agency (ADA) which in effect came under the Defence Research and Development Organisation (DRDO), and HAL was made a sub-contractor to ADA!. Meanwhile the original concept of the LCA also underwent change. There was strong pressure from the scientific community to include the latest technologies which we did not have in the country and, hence, this lure of high technology, so common in the aviation profession, led to the desire, approved by the Air Force, for a complex design of the aircraft, far beyond the capabilities of the country at that time, with predictable problems and time and cost overruns. This was made more complex by the IAF withdrawing from the programme for nearly eight years (when it was designated as a "technology demonstrator") since IAF experts concluded that the Project Definition Phase (PDP) could not be met. Two decades later, it is clear that while we have an aircraft flying, the original ASR (Air Staff Requirement), which was heavily influenced by the scientific community, in favour of greater technological complexity, cannot be met. We also failed to take our lessons from the HF-24 design seriously and went ahead to design an aircraft around an unknown engine, the Kaveri, which was expected to have been perfected twenty years ago! As an interim solution, we relied on an uncertain supply (at that time from the US while we were under severe sanctions) of the GE-404 engines, 11 of which were supplied after the US President authorised a special waiver. Perhaps the table of IAF acquisitions at Appendix A can inform the reader of the core issues in the aircraft industry during the past 62 years.

This has been changing during the past decade and new opportunities are opening up, with a sustained high economic growth on one side and access to new sources of technology and arms on the other. But major institutional and structural reforms would be required to take advantage of the new opportunities. Our institutional mechanisms have come up in bits and pieces and have been adequate for licensed production of aircraft and weapons. But this mortgages the country's security to the policies of the suppliers every time the aircraft or weapon completes its design life.

The greatest challenge ahead of us is how to strengthen design and development of aircraft and associated systems ranging from aero-engine to radars, weapons and all the innumerable components inside the aircraft. As our study indicates, it is this process that has not received the required attention.[2] In trying to rectify the situation, what remains (or should remain) uppermost in the minds of everyone is that the Indian Air Force is the major stakeholder in the

---

2.   For example, the DGOF (Director General Ordnance Factories) had even set up a design bureau for producing new weapons and this is one of the reasons it has never been able to supply arms and ammunition to the IAF beyond rifles and their ammunition.

aircraft industry since finally it is its aircrew who have to face the challenges to defend the country even with their life if required and its technical crews have to maintain the aircraft for operational tasks at peak performance. Since design and development should be integral to the production agency, an integrated seamless organisation is required.

One approach would be to adopt the pattern existing in the Indian Navy since the 1950s where the Indian Navy has within its headquarters a Directorate of Naval Design that undertakes the warship designs and modification to designs [along with systems integration and design by the Weapons and Electronic System Engineering Establishment (WESEE)]. Naval HQ also has a Controller of Warship Production so that the construction is monitored and managed properly, mostly with naval officers at the head of the dockyards which actually construct the warships. By 2006, out of 80 warships constructed indigenously, 50 were designed by the Indian Navy's Design Directorate. It is now well into design and construction of the Naval HQ designed aircraft carrier (called ADS, that is, Air Defence Ship) of 38,000 ton displacement at the Cochin Shipyard.

The second approach would be to establish an Aeronautics Commission under a Department of Aeronautics on the pattern of the Space and Atomic Energy Departments. A number of proposals have been made in the past and supported at fairly high levels by people of great competence, credibility and integrity. It is time to look at these for a more coordinated approach to the aviation industry in the future because of the tremendously advanced technology that is involved, the greatly enhanced role of air power in modern warfare as well as in peace, besides the enormously increased costs involved. Growth of the aviation industry is critical not only for the future defence of India, but also for its broader national technological and economic needs.

This volume is a humble attempt to trace the history and status of the aircraft industry in India. In the writing of this volume, I have received enormous help and support from many people and my gratitude goes to them all. I am grateful to my colleagues at the Centre for Air Power Studies for their help, particularly in bearing up with my preoccupation with the work in researching and writing this volume while trying to manage this Centre. Above all, I would to like to specifically acknowledge the moral and material support of HAL without which this enterprise would not have seen the light of day. I wish to state that I alone am responsible for any errors and omissions, besides the conclusions drawn in the volume.

I am glad its publication has coincided with 100 years since aviation came to India first in 1910, and also HAL being 70 years old this year. I hope you will find the volume useful, while I must think of taking the subject forward to evolve the necessary concepts for the Indian aircraft industry in the 21st century.

Air Commodore **Jasjit Singh** (Retd)
Director, Centre for Air Power Studies
New Delhi

Appendix A

Aircraft Acquired by IAF Since 1947

Aircraft Type	Designed in India	Licensed Manufactured	Outright Purchased
Trainers	HT-2	Percival Prentice	Harvard/T-6G
	HJT-16 Kiran	Tiger Moth	Iskara
	HPT-32		BAe Hawk
Fighters	HF-24 Marut	Vampire	Toofani
	LCA (under ADA design)	Gnat	Mystere IVA
		MiG-21 FL/M/bis	Hunter 56
		Jaguar	MiG-21 (250 a/c)
		MiG-27 ML	Su-7
		BAE Hawk	Mirage 2000H
		Su-30MKI	MiG-29
			Su-30MK
			MiG-23BN
			MiG-23MF
			MiG-27ML
			MiG-25
Transport	NIL	B-24 Liberator	Dakota
		Avro HS-748	Packet C-119G
		Do 228	An-12
			Super Constellation
			DHC Caribou
			DHC Otter
			IL-14
			An-32
			IL-76
			IL-78

1

Descent into Darkness
The Raj and India's Deindustrialisation

Long years ago, we made a tryst with destiny, and now the time comes when we shall redeem our pledge, not wholly or in full measure, but very substantially. At the stroke of the midnight hour, when the world sleeps, India will awake to life and freedom. A moment comes, which comes but rarely in history, when we step out from the old to the new, when an age ends, and when the soul of a nation, long suppressed, finds utterance. It is fitting that at this solemn moment, we take the pledge of dedication to the service of India and her people and to the still larger cause of humanity.

At the dawn of history, India started on her unending quest, and trackless centuries are filled with her striving and the grandeur of her success and her failures. Through good and ill fortune alike, she has never lost sight of that quest or forgotten the ideals which gave her strength. We end today a period of ill fortune and India discovers herself again. The achievement we celebrate today is but a step, an opening of opportunity, to the greater triumphs and achievements that await us. Are we brave enough and wise enough to grasp this opportunity and accept the challenge of the future?

— Jawaharlal Nehru
Independence Speech, August 15, 1947

India has come a long way since Jawaharlal Nehru stated this in his address to the nation when India stepped into its freedom as a sovereign state at midnight of August 14-15, 1947. From a large number of perspectives, it was the best of times, and it was also the worst of times. Independence held out the promise of freedom and self-rule, an end to subjugation to an imperial power, and the hope of a better life and its quality into the future. But the fateful event that millions had waited for through long years of misery also partitioned the country on the basis of religion to create a new country with Muslim majority areas of erstwhile India ruled directly by the British, while leaving half of the country composed of princely states in a state of limbo of which two major states, J&K (Jammu and Kashmir) and Hyderabad posed serious challenges that have not disappeared even six decades later with respect to the former state. But the historical event was also marred by the tragedy of massive communal riots in north India, especially in the provinces of Punjab and Bengal where the boundaries of the new countries met, drawn as they were in New Delhi over maps in the offices of the imperial rulers far away from the people they affected or the lands they divided. No accurate records of the violence and carnage have been availalbe except that over three million human beings of different faiths — Muslim, Hindu, Sikh and Christian — were killed and a similar number crossed over the new boundary as a consequence of the creation of a new country called Pakistan (Land of the Pure) in a brutally historic ethnic cleansing. The partition has many implications for the region; but besides the reality of unprecedented human tragedy, it has also altered many of the historical realities. For want of space, we need not go into the numerous issues except that it fundamentally altered the dynamics of defence and parameters of power in both countries.

It had been obvious since World War I that the power if not the prestige of Great Britain, the sole superpower, and the imperial power that ruled India, had been waning since 1885. World War II left Britain economically impoverished, strategically weak, with military mutinies rearing their heads in its largest and comparatively the most powerful colony, India. It still ruled over its imperial colonies, though only notionally, with a number of them like Canada, Australia and New Zealand populated mostly by British migrants. The war had led to the rise of the United States (once a British colony) as a superpower, secure with vast oceans as its frontiers besides key military outposts on the littoral of these oceans. The Soviet Union had come out of World War II stronger than before in spite of having suffered acutely in the war. Within two years of the end of World War II, the Allies had split into two blocs: one led by the United States and the other by the Soviet Union, rapidly sliding into a Cold War that was to last 45 years, with some of its negative effects still haunting many countries with the proxy wars, exploitation and ideological militarised confrontation that had characterised the Cold War among the civilised 'developed' countries. Two issues deserve our attention in relation to the theme of our study. One, during the two decades after World War II, decolonisation of imperial rule spread across most of Asia and Africa. India's struggle for independence provided enormous momentum and motivation to other colonies, in effect, leading to India being accepted as a natural leader of the decolonising world. Second, and perhaps more important, the logical policy option for the contraction of British power across the world would have been to coopt as many of the erstwhile colonies within its sphere of influence. Obviously, the British expertise in global power management had led them toward this option; and India, the largest former colony and the "Jewel in the Crown" of the British Empire would have been an obvious choice to side with Britain.

London tried hard to get the Indian leadership to agree to the grant of "Dominion Status" to India before withdrawal from the colony to keep it under its influence, if not control.

But this was not acceptable to the Indian political leadership (essentially of the Indian National Congress) who wanted nothing less than *puran swaraj* (full independence, or sovereign status). The next best option for Britain was to keep India within the Commonwealth of Nations and here it succeeded because Nehru perceived advantages in this informal arrangement instead of the formal one. India at that time was certainly a weak power, but which was capable of exercising great influence in the international community because of the way it pursued its struggle for independence which provided a model for other colonies. It needs to be noted here that British and Western companies (engaged in manufacture and trade) dominated the economic scene in India and a complete break with Britain could hardly be seen to be in our interests in spite of being a country impoverished under British rule, at least until indigenous industrial capacity had grown.

Even before independence, Jawaharlal Nehru's personal charisma had exercised a remarkable influence on the leadership of the developing (colonised) as well as developed (colonial) countries; and Mahatma Gandhi stood out on the world stage as a colossus of non-violence in a world trying to recover from a gruesome World War with the ultimate use of the atomic bomb and the tragically catastrophic destruction that it resulted in. One example was the holding of the Asian Relations Conference in New Delhi five months before India attained independence to discuss and evolve an Asian way of managing conflict and international relations. The other was to try and pursue a policy of "non-alignment" (adopted by the Indian National Congress in 1939 before World War II as the guiding principle of policy) in relation to the militarised power blocs in military confrontation with each other and each one trying to rope in as many countries as possible within its sphere of influence or military alliance. Strategically, therefore, after India's independence, it would have been to Britain's advantage to retain a close relationship with India to strengthen its own claim to continuing influence and power in the international community. This, of course, would have served India's interests also. But it lost a major, historically significant opportunity to extend its influence by opting to side with the aggressor in 1947-48 (and afterward) against the victim in its rejection of the rule of law, the framework for which it had itself created in the Transfer of Power arrangements. Clearly, the "Kashmir issue" soon became part of the Cold War politics and Britain opted to play the Cold War game as a subsidiary middle power rather than retain its own influence to the extent that it could by supporting India, rather than Pakistan, being more comfortable with its militaristic ethos.

The reason we have delved into this aspect of India's independence is that it had a profound impact on the future of our country and its attempt to build a strong scientific and technological base. Briefly, the US tended to follow Britain's lead and advice concerning its former colonies on the assumption that the British had ruled these countries and, hence, would know them better! Hence, when the Kashmir issue and war erupted with the Pakistani invasion against the then independent state of J&K (which acceded to India on October 26, 1947, consistent with the Transfer of Power arrangements defined by the British before leaving India), India sent in its armed forces to Kashmir to defend what was now legally and politically Indian territory. The British, however, forgetting their own dispensation for transfer of power, supported Pakistan at the UN and even persuaded the United States to do so in spite of US Secretary of State George Marshall insisting, at least till April 1948, that as far as the US was concerned, the state had legally acceded to India.[1] This inevitably reduced India's confidence in Britain's impartiality and willingness to build closer relations with India and, consequently, increased the mutual distrust which was in bad need of reduction. New Delhi continued its linkages with Britain on a range of issues, including weapons and equipment and potential military and techno-economic cooperation.

One of the important manifestations of this phenomenon was that India regularly turned to Britain for advice on how to organise the development of its science and technology base for greater capacity and capability, especially in defence. Eminent scientists visited India to study its problems and rendered reports but which *prima facie* hardly helped matters. One of the central problems, of course, was that India had been almost totally deindustrialised in the 250-year rule by the British into a raw material supplier rather than a manufacturer, leave alone an inventor or a designer. The imperatives of World War II as it impinged on India's eastern frontier, did demand greater attention than was given to them, especially since some rudimentary defence production and testing facilities had been set up by the mid-19th century and aviation had come to India by 1912, and an aircraft factory had been set up by 1939 by private enterprise as a joint venture between American and Indian businessmen. But before we deal with those issues, it is important to briefly survey India's economic, scientific technological and industrial base before, and at the time of, independence and assess its needs and policy priorities in that context.

Impact of Colonisation

That India was a major economic power in earlier centuries is a historical reality, no doubt reinforced by the fact that the British and other European powers did not come to India and stay for more than two centuries only to enjoy the hot and humid climate, but in reality to make money and build an empire. India had a strong manufacturing industry in the pre-machine age and its share of global manufacturing output in the early 18th century was nearly 25 percent, with China as the only country ahead of it at nearly 33 percent of the global manufacturing output (see Fig. 1.1 which shows the comparative figures for four countries). The national income of these four countries also was roughly in the same proportion. By the middle of the 18th century, the Industrial Revolution was beginning to grow and expand from England to Europe and North America, leading ultimately to industrialisation of war. The end result was that with the Industrial Revolution came a number of parallel phenomena.

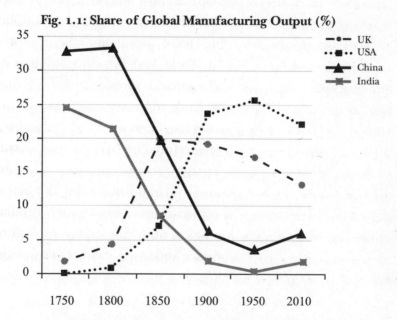

Fig. 1.1: Share of Global Manufacturing Output (%)

Source: Based on Paul Kennedy, *The Rise and Fall of Great Powers*
(New York: Random House, 1987), p. 149.

Firstly, Britain rapidly acquired superior technology for civil and military purposes which soon spread to the other European and North American powers. This was the major factor for the rise of imperial colonisation of Asian, Africa and Latin America with the combined effects of superior military capabilities and the industrial means of economic productivity which destroyed indigenous industrial capacity that was not based on mechanisation. The expansion of colonialism, especially to regions with rich and vast material and human resources, also led to the affluence and "renaissance" of Europe, while the benefits of industrialisation were not only lost to the colonies, but their traditional means and methods of economic productivity, especially in manufacturing output, regressed. Even China lost out on industrialisation under the Japanese and Western hegemony and control. This had a far-reaching impact on the quality of life of the people and economic progress of the country. The human and material resources were drained off to work in the interests of the colonial powers. For example, after the mid-19th century, Britain set up huge plantations across its empire from Fiji to Burma (Myanmar), Malaya, Ceylon (Sri Lanka), South and East Africa all the way to the West Indies, with physical labour from India, the descendants of whom are still struggling for their rights in many cases. The medieval slave "trade" acquired new dimensions compared to the earlier periods. The overall impact was the impoverishment of the masses through the colonial "drain of wealth" from India to Britain over the course of the 19th century. This drain in 1882 was estimated to have amounted to Rs. 1,355 million (in 1946-47 prices) working out to more than 4 percent of the national income that year.[2] In essence, this was no different from other invaders of earlier centuries who looted and returned to their own country as distinct from those invaders who occupied India, even built empires and ruled it and, in turn, were absorbed into the Indian civilisation. Mohammad Ghauri and Nadir Shah symbolise the former while the Mughals represent the latter, which also enriched the Indian civilisation and culture while improving its manufacturing output.

We can see the difference also in agriculture — the main source of economic productivity which employed over 70 percent of the national workforce for most of the period till independence. While economic data has not been consistent and reliable, we may look at historical evidence for clues. There is little or no mention of any famines during the ancient times down to the Mughal Empire except in the northern half of the Deccan plateau which lies along the fault-lines of the southwest monsoon and, hence, is prone to erratic rainfall in a rain-fed agricultural economy which created such conditions. The fertile and productive Indo-Gangetic plains hardly experienced famines even in years when the overall monsoons were weak. But during the British rule, there had been a large number of famines in the 19th and 20th centuries, the last one being the "Great Bengal famine" in 1943-45 when 3.8 million lives were lost. The British had set up a Commission in 1880 after the famines in north India, especially in Punjab in 1870 and 1890. Except for the handful of canals built during the Afghan regimes in the pre-Mughal period and small reservoirs across the country since times immemorial, agriculture had remained essentially rain-fed till 1900 AD. The area under irrigation doubled between 1900 and 1939, with water from a number of new canals built during this period mostly in West Punjab (now in Pakistan) besides new reservoirs built in some of the princely states like Gwalior and Mysore. But this was inadequate to ward off the Bengal famine partly because of foodgrain diversion for the British Armies (including the 2.6 million strong Indian troops) fighting during World War II in Europe, North Africa and Asia. Close to the end of the colonial period, the average per capita availability of foodgrain was about 400 grams,[3] with life expectancy being in the order of 32.5 years. Per capita income had risen between 1871 and 1911 but had stagnated after that.

This is the root cause of underdevelopment of developing countries in general and India in particular, which did not then have access to the fruits of industrialisation. In India, the impact on the extremely poor health and medical capabilities may be judged from the facts that population growth between 1871-1951 was a mere 0.60 percent per annum (with the absolute figure of population of the subcontinent increasing from 249 million in 1871 to 382 million in seven decades) although the average number of births among women of child-bearing age was six! It is not surprising that life expectancy hovered around a mere 20 years till the 1940s, moving up only in the last two decades before independence to reach 34.9 years by 1951.[4] Literacy rates during the two-century British rule remained around 9 percent till 1941 when they started to increase slowly.

Second, Britain was able to colonise India, mostly through trading rights and military-technical superiority. While many claims have been made about the "benign" rule of the British, empirical data shows that even during the first half of the 20th century, the rate of growth of national income averaged a pathetic 0.99 percent per year during the period 1900-46 (with negative growth during the decade in which World War I took place).[5] Not surprisingly therefore, per capita income growth in constant prices during this period averaged 0.21 percent per year, remaining negative for three of the four decades.

Third, and most relevant to our current study, historically, India has been an agrarian-pastoral civilisation. Over centuries, a stable (though not necessarily egalitarian) economic and social system provided adequate means of livelihood to the masses with a miniscule proportion of the affluent but who (mostly) also supported and promoted craftsmen, artisans and other professionals who not only provided the sources of the remarkable manufacturing output but also the basis of art and culture. This is how India has been so rich in architecture, music, etc. for over more than two millennia.[6]

Indian industrial capacity based on the pre-industrial model of craftsmanship was rapidly destroyed and the country was, in essence, *deindustrialised* from which it is now beginning to recover. India, in this process, became a raw materials exporting country, mostly to Britain, while importing manufactured products. This was most visible in a number of key fields like steel where iron ore was exported to England and India imported wrought iron and finished steel for the needs of the railways and other necessities. Similarly, Indian superior handspun cloth gave way to imported cloth from the textile mills of Britain. The overall situation has been summed up succinctly: "The Indian handicraft sector was certainly large in absolute terms at the beginning of the colonial period (before the Industrial Revolution really started to impact the world), supplying perhaps a quarter of world production of manufactured goods in 1750, and during the nineteenth century, manufacturing activity in India remained almost entirely confined to handicrafts — modern factories employed less than 5 percent of the manufacturing workforce as late as 1901."[7] As the 1880 Famine Commission concluded, by the middle of the century,

> ...at the root of much of the poverty of the people of India and of the risks to which they are exposed in seasons of scarcity lies the unfortunate circumstance that agriculture forms almost the sole occupation of the mass of the population, and that no remedy for present evils can be complete which does not include the introduction of a diversity of occupations, through which the *surplus population may be drawn from agricultural pursuits and led to find the means of subsistence in manufactures or some such employment*[8] (emphasis added).

There is little evidence that this was taken up seriously by the British Indian government, perhaps because the roots of the malaise lay in the upheaval of the established socio-economic institutions of the pre-British Raj days, though, no doubt, also affected by the progressive dissolution of the Mughal Empire before that. The history of the deindustrialisation process is long and painful. In the final analysis, not only did the Indian (and Chinese) share of total world manufacture shrink relatively, simply because of the West's output was rising so swiftly, but in some cases, their manufacturing capabilities and economies declined absolutely, that is, they deindustrialised, because of the penetration of their traditional markets by the far cheaper and better products of the Lancashire factories. After 1813 (when the East India Company's trade monopoly ended), imports of cotton fabrics into India rose spectacularly, from one million yards (1814) to 51 million yards (1830) to 995 million yards (1870), driving out many of the traditional domestic producers in the process.[9] Industrial Revolutions, whereever they have occurred, have inevitably involved changes besides those that are limited to technical processes and products.

Detailed and authoritative accounts of the history of the process of deindustrialisation of India are now available. We don't intend going into the details here. Suffice it to state that limited scale industry based on the factory system, employing machines driven by coal and steam, with mechanical means of production, started in India very hesitantly, with little encouragement from the British Indian government, more than a century after the Industrial Revolution had been well established in Europe and North America. Meanwhile, the Indian economy had already suffered serious debilities. Factory system enterprises had been established till the 1860s by the

East India Company or the private British merchants (after 1813 when the monopoly of the East India Company was abolished); both being primarily traders, "they had produced nothing but a commercial revolution in India. An Industrial Revolution might have been expected to follow in the next fifty or seventy years, but we find instead machines and machine-made goods being imported from Great Britain in ever increasing quantities, a handful of specialised industries being built, and indigenous manufacturing being destroyed in that process."[10] Advances in technology in Europe further regressed India's foreign trade. For example, introduction of synthetic colours completely wiped out India's indigo production and trade within a decade. But the East India Company or the other European traders sought larger profits from import of synthetic colours rather than establish capacity in India.

S. Pollard writes that Industrial Revolutions "... are marked by the emergence of an engineering industry, to create and maintain the new equipment and the motors or engines needed by the first industries to be mechanised: this, in turn, depends on an iron (or steel) industry, a second typical feature; and together, they demand new sources of power, coal, oil or hydro-electric installations."[11] At the same time, extensive creation and sustenance of infrastructure and the growth of what has been termed as "primary sectors" which would lead to the derived growth sectors are vital to such revolutions. But no major advance in any of these sectors is possible without parallel advances in the others which involves a great pressure "to accumulate in real terms, the large resources required for simultaneous investment in different sectors."[12] There was a great deficit of these resources, which, creamed off by British imperial policy goals, were not available in the country. Professor Lewis believed in a minimum saving rate of 12 percent for an Industrial Revolution, which was far above what was available in India where the gross saving rate barely came up to around 6 percent by 1947, by which time some industry had been established in the country. Thus, the few industries which could garner foreign capital during the British period were all export oriented and even the railways were built with commercial profit as the ultimate objective. India as a British colony could not adopt the measures to garner resources that other countries in the West did in addition to using the resources of their colonies. For British India, the only solution was import and balanced investment of British capital which was not forthcoming in quantities or on conditions that could have provided the necessary capabilities.

India could not develop heavy industries during the 19th century not only because of capital shortage, but also because of lack of high grade iron ore and inadequate production of coal (in spite of the country's enormous reserves of coal) due to lack of machine-based processes of extraction and processing. Thus, even by the end of the century, all the iron and steel required for the Indian railways, textile mills, every mechanical appliance needed in the country, etc. was imported from Britain even while the raw materials were exported from India. Only one coal mine was functional till 1840. More than a century after the Industrial Revolution had been ushered in on the basis of coal and iron, India was importing about 600,000 tons of coal annually in 1880, compared to indigenous production of around 470,000 tons, grossly inadequate to meet even the requirement of the railways when locomotives were run on coal-fed boilers and steam. Even in this framework, while the Industrial Revolution was triggered in Britain by the growth of the coal, iron and steel industries, India's industrialisation followed more than a century later, with the application of steam to the jute and cotton mills. It was this chronic deficit in heavy industry (like steel, power, etc,) that the government set about giving priority to after independence which then spawned industrial capacity to a range of areas and capabilities.

The foregoing is not meant to suggest that no machine-based manufacturing was established in India during the Raj. But even in this respect, the mainstay of "industrialisation" during the bulk of the colonial period was textile mills. In fact, the first textile mill was set up in 1856 (a century after the Industrial Revolution had impacted Europe) and the number of mills increased to 47 in 1875, going up to 79 in 1883. But the initial growth was based on export oriented production, progressively moving on to integrated mills that could produce both yarn and cloth. However, with the onset of World War I, much of the textile exports came to an end. It also needs to be noted that the textile industry had to rely on "relentless improvisation in the use of old machinery ..." indicating the basic weakness in the process of reindustrialisation: that of design and development based on access to new technology.[13]

The cotton industry had held the centre-stage in expositions and explanations of India's industrial progress during the colonial period. But, as Pollard stated, an Industrial Revolution depends on the emergence of an engineering industry which, in turn, depends upon an iron and steel industry and together they demand sources of uninterrupted power. At the same time, it requires economic investments which were not forthcoming in view of the drain of wealth from India to Britain to provide for its rise to greater power. Hence, a brief look at the development of these industries in India during the colonial period is essential to understand the challenges at the time of independence.[14] The iron and steel industry had begun to grow, largely based on the private initiatives of a handful of Indian businessmen.

Manufacture of iron products by traditional methods was a well established trade at the beginning of the colonial period; and it was so also at the end of that period, being carried out by hereditary non-agricultural craftsmen (mostly tribals and gypsies) to meet the needs of agriculture and the rural market. The first "iron works" was set up in 1874. The Bengal Iron Works Company started production in 1877. The company had a chequered career and it was a modest producer by the time of World War I, with no potential for expansion because of lack of capital and, finally, was producing only cast iron pipes before it stopped production in 1925. The Indian Iron and Steel Company (IISCO) was established in 1918 to produce pig-iron for export to Japan and the USA in the early 1920s.

But it was the Tata family which established the Tata Iron and Steel Company (TISCO) in 1907 (after preparations during the previous eight years) which really may be considered as the foundation of the Industrial Revolution in India — two and a half centuries after Britain. The model established was a unique example at that time of a successful large scale innovative industrial enterprise which is more than valid for today and contains many lessons for the future of the aircraft industry in India. The Tatas had the advantage of benefiting from the experience of their family concern, Tata Sons and Company, being the largest importer of iron and steel at that time. They already owned cotton mills and other industrial enterprises and had offices in potential export markets in China and Japan. The new plant was thoroughly researched and planned in all respects, including availability of coking coal, iron ore and water. Most important of all, *technology transfer was arranged by hiring skilled foreign personnel,* rather than using consultants.[15]

The number of foreign specialist workers peaked at 229 by the mid-1920s and these were replaced by trained cadres of the Tatas' Indian employees.[16] Finance was raised from equity capital subscribed by family members, fellow businessmen and rulers of princely states. Later on, the government became the major customer of TISCO in order to meet the requirements of the railways so necessary to manage its Indian empire and its trade; and, hence, ensured protection of the industry to enable it to face global competition where the foreign producers were receiving government subsidies. TISCO's efficiency may be judged from the fact that the output per man rose seven-fold between 1919 and 1939.[17]

By 1923, TISCO was supplying about 30 percent of the Indian market for steel, including two-thirds of the government's purchases of steel rails. TISCO was also producing pig-iron for export to supplement demands from its steel production. The industrial depression of the early 1930s did severe damage in Europe and North America largely since they were developed and industrialised; but it bypassed India to a great extent since India had little to lose except its poverty. (The recent global "meltdown" of financial and economic capacity of those countries and India's relative success in dealing with it is similar to the 1930s' depression in that respect). By the late 1930s, TISCO was meeting two-thirds of the total (and increasing) consumption of finished steel in India. British steel producers were worried by the early 1930s about the future sales of their products in India and decided that it would be to their benefit to come to some arrangements with TISCO which would bring it into the imperial market sharing cartel agreements than by other means, including direct competition in India. This led to a series of agreements underpinned by official agreements in

1932-34. In the final analysis, it should be recognised that the colonial government was more sympathetic to TISCO as compared to other manufacturing companies because of the strategic requirements and the income generated by the railway system which had suffered from the supply crisis of World War I, making local manufacture more important in order to sustain colonial rule.

Defence Industry

By the middle of World War I, the strategic necessity of industrial development became obvious. At the same time, domestic political pressures led by the Indian National Congress leaders like Motilal Nehru (Jawaharlal's father), Madan Mohan Malaviya and others started to mount pressure for a broader process of industrialisation in India (as much as the pressures for "Indianisation" for the armed forces). In response to these demands, the government set up an Industrial Commission to examine future policy options. The *Report of the Indian Industrial Commission 1916-18,* pressed the government to play an active part in the industrial development of the country and make it more self-sufficient in a wide range of goods instead of relying on imports. Two factors had gone into the establishment of the Commission: one was the insistent and unanimous nationalist opinion that had grown in previous decades that Britain had deliberately neglected industrial advancement in India, and the other was the British experience during World War I, with India cut off from the Western world and, except for the very substantive military manpower, unable to assist in the war effort in industrial terms since it lacked a defence industry and its weapons had to be imported. The Commission summarised some of the main points as follows:[18]

The blanks in our industrial catalogue are of a kind most surprising to one familiar only with European conditions. We have already alluded to the basic deficiencies in our iron and steel industries, and have explained how, as a result of these, the many excellent engineering shops in India are mainly devoted to repair work, to the manufacture, hitherto mainly from imported materials, of comparatively simple structures, such as roofs and bridges, wagons and tanks. India can build a small marine engine and turn out a locomotive, provided certain essential parts are obtained from abroad, but she has not a machine to make nails or screws, nor can she manufacture some of the essential parts of electrical machinery. Electrical plants and essential parts of electrical machinery are still, therefore, imported, in spite of the fact that incandescent lamps are used by the millions and electrical fans by the tens of thousands. India relies on foreign supplies for steel springs and iron chains, and for wire ropes, a vital necessity of the mining industry. We have already pointed out the absence of any manufacture of textile machinery, and with a few exceptions, even of any manufacture of textile mill accessories.

Few industries could rely on local recruitment for supervisory personnel: the working class had little education to graduate into such positions, while the educated classes were unfit for them because of the absence of the requisite technical education. The report concluded that "circumstances of India had made it necessary for us to devise proposals which will bring the State into far more intimate relations with industrial enterprise" than before.[19] The main recommendations of the report included a focus on the government to establish technical education suited to practical industrial requirements and provide technical and scientific information services, besides encouraging private agencies to provide industrial finance.

Unfortunately, like the recommendations of the Famine Commission four decades earlier, little came out of it except that in the *1919 Government of India Act,* industrial policy was devolved to the provincial governments which had neither the resources nor the incentive to pursue this goal. The central government was left without the revenues to pursue any serious industrialisation beyond the general support to TISCO (which was more in pursuant to the strategic and financial interests of the Raj rather than the people of India). By 1939, over a quarter of the value of all railway stores, and almost half the value of stores for state railways, were bought from firms operating in India (though all of them were not manufacturing them).

Britain as the sole superpower since the mid-19th century till the eve of World War II, possessed the largest empire in the world, but it could not support a war against the combined industrial might of Germany and Japan due to its failure, or unwillingness, to industrialise India as the bulwark of its power east of Suez. Perhaps due to the consciousness of the Great Mutiny of 1857-58, the exceptions comprised the railways and telegraph, etc. in India which had been laid (since 1854)[20] in a manner best suited to serve colonial military and commercial needs. Due to the depletion of resources, Britain had adopted a defence planning guidance policy of "no war in the next ten years" in the late 1930s. Similarly, flowing from the earlier East India Company's strategic policy directive, adopted by the Crown with even greater conviction, the Indian military on the eve of World War II, was left with obsolescent weapons and equipment of World War I vintage, and there was no defence industrial base in the country. But even after the Munich Summit with Adolf Hitler in September 1938 and Neville Chamberlain's famous remarks from the balcony of 10 Downing Street, to the British military leadership, a war with Germany and Italy appeared to loom large — a war, Britain believed it would lose, especially if access to the military capabilities of its colonies was denied by the enemy. And India in this respect was expected to be the mainstay of the imperial war effort.

In October 1938, the Committee of Imperial Defence met and concluded that the vast oceans (North Atlantic, Mediterranean Sea and Indian Ocean) controlled possibly by Germany and Italy would make the empire, especially its "Jewel in the Crown" (India), inaccessible to London.[21] India, with its population of 360 million, was the most important source of manpower, and a crucial asset which could be lost if Japan entered the war and the Axis powers controlled and closed Britain's access to this vital source while it was fighting to defend itself from a possible invasion. The answer, the British concluded, could be found in India, in the most important part of the empire. "British military planners regarded the expansion of India's defence infrastructure as the best means of preserving their country's empire."[22] But with insensitivity typical of British imperial military leaders and administrators, they did not think it necessary to consult the major political parties and their leaders in India. The consequence was that at a time when the British Prime Minister was talking of peace in our time, the Indian political leaders understandably regarded the plans to expand India's defence infrastructure with deep suspicion and hostility.

The Japanese invasion of Southeast Asia, and from Burma into India, made things far more complicated after "Fortress Singapore" fell along with the sinking of the battleship *Prince of Wales* and the battle cruiser *Repulse* by Japanese carrier-borne aircraft bombing in the early stages of the Japanese advance into Southeast Asia. The British colonies of Singapore, Malaya and Burma fell rapidly to the advancing Japanese forces. The Burma Army put up a gallant defence but was overwhelmed by the speed and numerical and technological superiority of the Japanese forces. There was very little air power that Britain could deploy against the near total air superiority that the Japanese air power possessed. The Indian Air Force (IAF) deployed its single squadron, No. 1 Squadron (which had been raised at a glacial pace over eight years, symbolising the government's low priority to defence of India and Indianisation of the military in the years before the war!), commanded by the great pioneer Squadron Leader K.K. "Jumbo" Majumdar at Tonguou on Burma's eastern border, gallantly attacked (in the slow moving Lysander reconnaissance aircraft locally modified to carry two 250-lb bombs each) and damaged the Japanese bomber base across the border in February 1942.

India in 1938 was grossly unprepared for war. This had been so in spite of the fact that the Mesopotamian campaign of 1916, conducted directly under New Delhi's responsibility, mostly with Indian military forces, had failed to achieve any notable success. This was primarily due to the Indian military establishment not having made any attempt to adapt to modern technology and tactics compared to the forces of the Ottoman Empire. For example, the chief mode of transportation of the Indian Army was still horse power; and officers lacked telephones even at headquarters! The Army in India (Esher) Committee appointed in 1919 did recommend that the Indian Army be made responsible directly to the British government rather than to the Viceroy as this would also enable Britain to build military capability outside the arms control regulated forces in Europe during the inter-war years. This, however, was turned down by the government in New Delhi which was interested in reducing the defence budget, not increasing it. But the lessons learnt had not been applied in India during the inter-War period. And now the time between the Chatfield Committee report and the onset of a war across the globe was too short to rectify the deficiencies in the defence industrial sector, created by both policy and neglect. The government owned armament industry was miniscule. There was no indigenous/private arms industry. Scientific and technical capacity, small as it was, was set up mostly by the initiative of princely states and Indian businessmen. The total manufacturing capability for military equipment comprised the government's six ordnance factories which barely produced enough military equipment to keep a peace-time force operational. In 1936-37, India imported Rs. 100.5 million (US$ 30.2 million) worth of arms, mostly from Britain. New Delhi had been insisting since 1933 that new expenditures on the modernisation of the armed forces should be made primarily in the context of the "Indian Mutiny". Not surprising, therefore, that the six ordnance factories produced saddles, uniforms, rifles and small arms ammunition even in the late 1930s, suited more to the Army's constabulary role than to function as an imperial "strategic reserve" for use against a major power.[23]

In a parallel effort to the Chatfield Committee's working, a number of other committees submitted their own assessments, especially since the British officers in the Indian Defence Headquarters feared that the Indian Army would be no match for an enemy if Britain deployed it in the service of the empire. In 1938, the War Office established a committee under Major General H.R. Pownall, its Director of Operations and Intelligence, to examine the strength of Indian defences and make recommendations to enhance them. The committee found that the defence forces in India were "still based on the strategical (*sic*) situation as it existed fifteen years ago" and made a series of recommendations regarding placing a dedicated Army division and four Air Force squadrons for the defence of imperial communications outside India. In order to support its proposals, the committee concluded that "some degree of modernisation of the Army in India is imperative," and that "India should, as soon as possible, be made self-sufficient in respect of supplies of warlike material so far as may be found practicable,"[24] The British Chiefs of Staff endorsed the report, though the financial burden promised to be very high. The Defence Department of the Government of India conducted a separate cost analysis and concluded that these reforms would require an initial investment of Pounds sterling 40 million (equivalent to one-sixth of the British defence budget), exceeding the estimates of the British Chief of Staff who believed around Pounds 29 million would be sufficient.

Meanwhile, Major General Claude Auchinleck, at that time the Deputy Chief of General Staff of the Indian Army, was critical of the Pownall Report and considered it impractical. Instead, in a report submitted in October 1938, he provided an assessment of the Indian defence establishment, questioning India's ability to support the war effort. Not only was there no private armament producing capability, the country also lacked the basic industries essential to the production of armaments that could support an armament industry if started by the government. Very little of the raw materials essential for the production of armaments was available in the country. However, the Auchinleck Committee strongly recommended that London should not only modernise the Indian armed forces, but also expand the domestic ordnance factories to enable India to supply at least the small arms and ammunition for the updated formations. Since India had no automobile industry (three decades after Europe had started to rapidly expand theirs), more vehicles would have to be obtained from Britain, Canada and the United States. Weapons like the anti-aircraft artillery and anti-tank guns would be uneconomical and, hence, would have to be imported.

In order to provide an independent set of recommendations and also reconcile the proceedings and recommendations of these two committees, the British Cabinet set up the "Expert Committee on the Defence of India" (also known as the "Chatfield Committee" after its Chairman, Lord Chatfield, the First Sea Lord) in October 1938. The title was misleading in the sense that the committee serving the Cabinet was to draw up plans for *all British possessions* in Asia. India's importance as a market and source of raw material had declined over the previous century, but its manpower and potential as a military base had remained. However, imperial policies and neglect had ensured that India was far less prepared, and these reforms had little scope of being implemented. Chatfield argued that during the 19th century, Britain had maintained the strength of its naval power at least equal to the combined capability of the next two major naval powers till World War I. But after the war, it could at best match one naval power and the naval priority would obviously go to the immediate needs of Britain to keep the sea lanes open in the Atlantic and the Mediterranean. This only reemphasised the importance of India in defending the empire. But India's deindustrialisation under the Raj now became the most serious problem for the British Empire. Auchinleck had estimated a four to five-year period to build up Indian defence, and the Chatfield Committee's estimate of a five-year period for building up imperial defence centred on India came too late (war between Britain and Germany was declared less than a year after the committee began its deliberations) and, hence, contributed little to the growth of the defence industry in India that could support the imperial war effort. Appeasement was to have bought time; but even before the fruits of appeasement could translate into effective results, it was clear that the luxury of time was simply not available.

While the Indian Army served with great distinction in the Allied campaigns in North Africa and Europe in the first three years of World War II, the arms supplies from India were grossly inadequate. The British challenge was made worse by the US Neutrality Act of 1937 which forbade the US from supplying any belligerent; but India was not in that list. On the other hand, it had no capacity beyond supplying food, cloth (the centrepiece of its fledgling industry) and small arms and ammunition. While the US Neutrality Act was not a hindrance for India, the limitation was the absence of defence industry in India. Hence, India itself turned to US supplies, especially for automotives and spares. The War Office in London was keen to maintain British standardisation throughout the empire. On the other hand, the Indian defence planners were not willing to let this hinder modernisation. By November 1939, the India Defence Department was arguing for increased use of North American vehicles in its armed forces, since they would also take less time to reach and were far more robust and sufficiently powerful to function effectively in Indian conditions. Sir Girija Shankar Bajpai, India's Agent General in Washington, in a meeting with P.H. Ailing, the Assistance Chief of the State Department's Division of Near East Affairs, on January 23, 1942, pointed out the advantages of America's deeper involvement with supporting expansion of India's defence industry. Bajpai argued that India could take care of the requirements of small arms, machine-guns and ammunition, but the deficiency in production in the heavier armament such as tanks and airplanes required American assistance. The Chatfield Plan for modernisation had recommended that "the vehicles should be as nearly as possible of the same type as those used by traders and private persons in India" in order to reduce the problem of spares.[25] Ford and General Motors were already manufacturing these products in the USA and Canada, and assembling them in Bombay. The Chatfield Report did not provide for vehicles to be manufactured in India but no one objected to the idea either.

The US sent a mission to India under the leadership of Henry Grady, a former Assistant Secretary of State in spring 1942. The Grady mission's report asserted that British efforts to industrialise India had not met the aims laid down earlier because "Britain's own urgent needs and the unreadiness of the government to clear the way for a rapid expansion of India's war industries led to (the) cancellation of a large part of the modernisation programme." The mission found the level of Indian armaments production unsatisfactory even in the case of manufacture of rifles to meet the Army's requirement, and recommended the establishment of a new rifle factory. The Grady mission was also critical of the three new plants set up for the production of armoured vehicles on the grounds that the Indian steel industry (which as noted earlier, was the major industry after textiles in colonial India) could produce armour plate for only 45 percent of the rate required and asked the government to rely further on Ford and General Motors. The mission recommended that the US provide more equipment to the Indian steel industry so as to increase its production.

It was inevitable that as the war progressed in Europe, India's defence industry would undergo some growth, and after the Japanese invasion of Southeast Asia, it expanded further. The number of ordnance factories increased from six to twenty-nine. In spite of British opposition, the American role in expansion of Indian defence industry to assist in the war effort against Japan grew after Pearl Harbour and the Japanese invasion and occupation of Burma.

While some growth of industrialisation did take place due to the demands of World War II, on the eve of independence virtually no industrial capacity, and even less access to modern science and technology, especially for design and development, existed in India after more than two centuries of the Industrial Revolution and colonial rule. The British maintained large military forces, equipment and bases. With a 40 percent share of central government expenditure (amounting to nearly 2-3 percent of national income), the largest item of current expenditure in peace-time was defence. But "this had a minimal effect on the demand for industrial goods since so little of the equipment used by the armed forces in India was manufactured locally."[26] One would imagine that World War II would provide a second opportunity to establish some defence industry in India. But, not surprisingly, barring the few workshops that catered to small arms and ammunition (for rifles and machine guns), no ordnance factories were set up in India, in the public or private sector. Even after Japan's entry into the war and its whirlwind offensive into Southeast Asia and Burma, the armed forces of the colonial regime relied on imports from Britain which itself was short of weapons and equipment.

Even in terms of general industrialisation which had begun through private enterprise, the British officials were unwilling to provide support, even after the Bengal famine. In January 1944, eight of India's most prominent businessmen, including J.R.D. Tata, the head of Tata Industries and Director of Hindustan Aeronautics Limited (HAL), G.D. Birla the prominent textile manufacturer (who had recently embarked on a venture with Nuffield to set up Hindustan Motors), and Thakurdas, the Director of the Reserve Bank of India, published *A Brief Memorandum Outlining a Plan of*

Economic Development for India in January 1944. They proposed
(in what came to be known as the "Bombay Plan") that the
government invest Rs. 1 billion (Pounds 75 million) in the
development of Indian industries after the war to enable per
capita income to be doubled within 15 years. However, the plan
never saw acceptance, opposed as it was by a large number of
British administrators, and Lord Wavell, the Viceroy of India,
thought the plan was "not convincing." Even a modified plan,
issued in 1945 after the war was over, found little acceptance
in the government. These developments also created a level
of friction between the Americans and Indian industrialists
who made it clear that their expectations were that India
should be able to maintain its autonomy while cooperating
with foreign collaboration. The original arrangements for
setting up HAL were seen as the appropriate framework for
post-war industrialisation.

The above is not to imply that India did not possess
any military-industrial capacity. The few ordnance factories
were expanded, especially after Japan entered the war and
the threat of its invasion against India appeared to be a
reality (besides the British need to drive the Japanese out
of British colonies in Southeast Asia). While India became
"self-sufficient" in small arms and ammunition by the end
of the war, it remained dependent on imports of heavy and
technologically advanced equipment like aircraft and tanks.
Between 1939-41, the total production of defence stores
(except uniforms, saddlery, etc) was 110,310 small arms
(0.303 rifles) and 382.3 million rounds for them at a time
when the Indian Army had begun to be expanded for war
with a strength that would soon touch 2.6 million men under
arms, and was being deployed in the Middle East and North
Africa. India also manufactured 1779,000 rounds of field

artillery shells and 112,000 rounds of medium artillery shells during this period. The peak annual production of selected munitions during World War II (along with that of Australia for comparison) is given below:

Table 1.1: Peak Annual Production of Selected Munitions During World War II for an Army of 2.6 Million

Item	India (1944-45)	Australia (1942-43)
Artillery pieces (3.7")	322	192
Artillery shells	2,475,492	2,679,000
Mortar shells	265,360	1,501,000
Grenades	908,340	1,901,000
Machine-guns	3,280	35,000
Rifles	164,034	137,685
Small arms ammunition	116,180	443,000
(in thousands of rounds)		

Source: Adapted from statistics in Intelligence Staff Study, "Maximum Forces Which Can Be Generated in the Indian Ocean in the Event of War," June 6, 1949, Department of the Army, NAR, P&O 370.01 TS, p. 7.

It may be useful here to look at the early history of the private aircraft industry in India when it started — and ended! (This is covered in more detail in a later chapter.) As noted earlier, an Indian entrepreneur, Walchand Hirachand and an American industrialist, William Douglas Pawley (who had put up China's first aircraft factory, and was planning to pull out of his China enterprise because of the war), met by chance on a flight across the Pacific Ocean and decided to establish a joint venture to design and develop aircraft in India. Thus, was born Hindustan Aircraft Ltd (HAL) later named Hindustan Aeronautics Ltd, with the Government of India and the Maharaja of Mysore acquiring 50 percent share and also giving land at Bangalore where the factory and the runway today stand. The management adopted the procedures found so useful by the Tatas, and employed American technicians along with Indians, with an American expert as the General Manager. It immediately set about designing and producing aircraft; the licence produced Harlow PC-5 trainer was soon flying by 1940, and the design of a fighter aircraft was started. The colonial government also became a shareholder in the company.

When the war in the Asia-Pacific expanded, the government took over the management of the factory from private control on the grounds of its being a strategic industry (queer logic that independent India would also adopt for defence equipment later). The Maharaja of Mysore waived his rights on the management board of the factory for the duration of the war, but for some reason, was not able to get it back after the war was over in August 1945. HAL was now tasked to repair and overhaul aircraft and engines for the US Army Air Force (USAAF) operating in the Eastern Theatre, including from India, to supply the Chinese forces fighting the Japanese in China in the historical "Over the Hump" air operations in northeast India. While the logic of overhaul is understandable, closing down the design and development of aircraft, especially fighter aircraft, constituted a retrograde step and even irresponsible, considering that soon after Pearl Harbour, the Japanese fleet had sailed into the Indian Ocean and bombed Madras city (now Chennai) before sailing along the coast, bombing other cities up to and including Calcutta (now Kolkata) before turning back. India was lying defenceless at that time. Though only a few bombs were dropped on Madras, the British Governor of Madras ordered a general evacuation from the city! But HAL remained limited to overhaul of American aircraft engines while the Indian Air Force and even the Royal Air Force in India kept importing aircraft from Britain (as, indeed, was the case with all military weapons and equipment during the colonial period). The few aircraft like the Mosquito fighter-bomber that HAL managed to build under licence were exported to China.

In the ultimate analysis, the 15 principal Indian defence industries did produce a significant proportion of the total requirement of the Army (there was no production of aircraft for use in India though, as stated above, some were built for export). In terms of real capabilities, most of these "industries" were no more than Army workshops and, hence, they reverted to their basic role and function after the war, leaving a mere six ordnance factories to survive by 1947 (though none existed in the area which became Pakistan). In addition, 14 railway workshops were engaged in the production of defence ancillary equipment which came to an end after the war.

To sum up, one can cite Professor B.R. Tomlinson of the University of Birmingham, who, in his landmark study of the Indian economy and industry since 1860, has stated:[27]

> Colonial bureaucrats did not stop to ask themselves the question, "What is the purpose of British rule in India?," but the underlying trend of their actions between 1860 and 1947 shows that they had an answer ready. Government policy, at least the `high policy' made on the telegraph lines between New Delhi and London, was meant to secure a narrow range of objectives of particular interest to the government itself, and in the attainment of which the actions of the government were all-important. This lowest common denominator of official concerns can be termed India's 'imperial commitment,' the irreducible minimum that the subcontinent was expected to perform in the imperial cause. This commitment was three-fold: to provide a market for British goods (he may have added, on terms suited to Britain), to pay interest on the sterling debt and other charges that fell due in London, and to maintain a large number of British troops from local revenues and make a part of the Indian army available for imperial garrisons and expeditionary forces from Suez to Hong Kong.

In essence, each of these commitments without the concurrence of the people of India cost the Indian treasury and sacrificed India's interests to those of Britain. Our purpose is not to condemn the British for they did rule in many areas with great sensitivity and not all of them were convinced of the policies being pursued. What we have sought to do is to carry out a brief survey of the unique coincident congruence of the decline and fall of the Mughal Empire and the rise of the British Empire which resulted in the Industrial Revolution passing India by and impoverishment of India in that process of deindustrialisation. It was this impoverishment-deindustrialisation of the country which independent India had to struggle against while technological advances increased exponentially and India was the target of sanctions on various counts, often while trying to pursue its national interests; we need to understand this so that we can reconcile the reindustrialisation of India with the context of the past.

Notes

1. For a detailed account of British policy and activism in support of the policy of siding with Pakistan, see C.D. Dasgupta, *War and Diplomacy in Kashmir* (New Delhi: Sage Publishers, 2002). Incidentally, the British Governor of the Northwest Province had "accepted" the accession of Gilgit and Hunza (an integral part of the state of Jammu & Kashmir, which had acceded to India on October 26, 1947) to Pakistan in November 1947, declared by Major Browne (in military service with the State Forces of Jammu & Kashmir) who had instigated and led the mutiny of Muslim troops, slaughtering the non-Muslim state troops in the area. See William A. Brown, *The Gilgit Rebellion 1947* (IBEX, 1998, privately produced and printed, not for sale).

2. Irfan Habib, "Studying a Colonial Economy – Without Perceiving Colonialism", *Modern Asian Studies*, March 19, 1985, pp. 375-6.

3. B.R. Tomlinson, *The Economy of Modern India 1860-1870* (Cambridge University Press, Indian Edition published by Foundation Books, New Delhi, 1998), p.7.

4. Here we must record that population growth rates after independence, especially after 1951, increased rapidly at as much as 3.2 percent per year because the government paid a great deal of attention to medical and health care to reduce infant mortality, but they were not matched by focus on controlling birth rates, with the result that a population explosion took place in the 1960s and 1970s. With low economic growth rates in the early decades and a high rate of population growth, it is clear that we were adding to poverty rather than eliminating it. With the current 8-9 percent growth of Gross Domestic Product (GDP) and a population growth of around 1.6 percent in the coming two decades, we can expect to increase per capita income growth at around 6-7 percent per year. This would provide a strong impetus to poverty elimination and raising the quality of life.

5. Tomlinson, n.3, p. 5.

6. A.L. Basham, *The Wonder That Was India* (New York: Grove Press Inc., 1954).

7. Tomlinson, n.3, p. 101, citing J. Krishnamurty, "Deindustrialisation in Gangetic Bihar During the Nineteenth Century: Another Look at the Evidence", *Indian Economic and Social History Review,* April 22, 1985, p.199.

8. Government of India, *Report of the Indian Famine Commission, 1880,* Part II, p. 171.

9. Paul Kennedy, *The Rise and Fall of the Great Powers* (New York: Random House, 1987), p. 148.

10. A. Tripathi, "Industry" in R.C. Majumdar (General Editor), *The History and Culture of the Indian People,* Vol. IX, *British Paramountcy and Indian Renaissance,* Part I (Bombay: Bharatiya Vidya Bhavan, 1963), p. 1095.

11. S. Pollard, "Investment, Consumption and the Industrial Revolution," *The Economic History Review,* second series, Vol. XI, No. 2, 1958, p. 217.

12. W.A. Lewis, *Theory of Economic Growth* cited in Tripathi, n.10, p. 1096.

13. Roy, "Size and Structure", *Indian Economic and Social History Review,* January 25, 1988.

14. Pollard, n.11.

15. William A. Johnson, *The Steel Industry in India* (Cambridge, Mass 1966), p. 245. cited in Tomlinson, n.3, p. 129.

16. It may be noted that the aircraft industry started with a private Indo-American joint venture in 1939 and the British Government of India became a shareholder in it in 1940. Even later, in 1956-57, design and development of a multi-role combat aircraft, the HF-24 Marut, commenced with a joint Indo-German design team headed by Dr. Kurt Tank.

17. Israel applies this yardstick to judge the efficiency and cost-effectiveness of its defence industry.

18. *Report of the Indian Industrial Commission 1916-18,* Vol. I, reprinted edition (Calcutta, 1934), p. 55.

19. Ibid., p.243.

20. This followed the strategic direction laid down by the Board of Trustees of the East India Company in 1858 on the steps it must take for the control of its territories abroad in the future.

21. They don't seem to have taken the possibility of Japan entering the war against the Allies and capturing all the British territories east of India while destroying the Royal Navy's main assets in the east.

22. A. Martin Wainwright, *Inheritance of Empire: Britain, India and the Balance of Power in Asia, 1938-55* (Westport: Praeger, 1994), p. 12.

23. Ibid., p. 13.

24. "The Defence Problems of India and Composition of the Army and Royal Air Force in India, 12 May, 1938," IOR, L/WS/1/151. 40-41, cited in Ibid., p. 17.

25. Cited in Wainwright, n. 22, p. 21.

26. Tomlinson, n.5, p. 136.

27. Ibid., p. 149.

2

The Inheritance

As would be obvious from the previous chapter, India entered its independence era with enormous handicaps and challenges; but they also presented an unprecedented opportunity to rebuild India: Nehru had already provided that vision and would steer the country toward that vision personally for the first fifteen years. The challenges varied from lack of sufficient food for the country's then 360 million people, a figure which crossed the billion mark in 2003, virtually no industry worth the name, with its share of global manufacturing output having dropped from 24.8 percent in 1750 to a fraction of one percent; a very poor literacy rate; life expectancy at birth a mere 32 percent or so; a handful of institutions to impart education in the science and technology fields; more than 70 percent of the population engaged in agriculture and even a larger proportion living in rural areas; religion, caste system; superstitions and mythology largely dominating the social life which was stratified into a caste system going back thousands of years and which transcended religion, and so on. The country was divided almost equally among the British ruled India and the 564 states of India ruled by Maharajas, with treaties with the imperial power that came to an end with India's independence. India, of course, has changed enormously in most respects since then; but a great deal of the old India still exists across the country. Above all, it has proved all predictions of its failure wrong and has

continued through the decades, with governments formed
and functioning on the democratic principle and practice
surviving various aberrations.

But before we discuss the period during and after
independence, it is necessary to have a brief look at the civil
aviation in the period when India was a British colony, and at
the aircraft manufacturing capability created in those years.

Civil Aviation: The Early Years

Before we examine the processes of acquisition of technology
for the aircraft industry in independent India, it may be useful
from the historical point to briefly review the aircraft industry
in the early years before independence. Aviation and aircraft
had come to India pretty early after the Wright Brothers carried
out the first manned flight of the heavier than air machine
in December 1903. Britain managed the first two successful
flights in indigenous aircraft six years later (and three years
after France had flown its aircraft in 1906). Among the first
Indians to have taken an interest in aviation was the then
Maharaja of Patiala, Maharaja Bhupinder Singh, who had sent
his chief engineer to Europe to study the art and science of
aviation and manned aircraft and bring back a British built
Farman biplane and a two-seater Gnome-Bleriot monoplane,
when he returned in December 1910. According to Edmond
Petit who was the curator of the Air France Museum in Paris
in the early 1980s, Kieth Davies flew his Bleriot aeroplane on
December 10, 1910, at Allahabad, making it the first manned
flight in India. Another successful flight was reported by *The
Statesman*, over the Jamuna and the Ganges in a biplane on
December 17, 1910.

Subsequently, more flights were carried out in Calcutta
(now Kolkata), Madras (now Chennai) and other places,

some of which carried women passengers. The first military experiment was carried out on January 16, 1911, near Aurangabad, for aerial reconnaissance of troops manoeuvring on the ground which consisted of four cavalry brigades, and one infantry brigade along with 12 British Generals on the ground witnessing the experiments. The world's first air mail was carried in India at Allahabad on February 18, 1910, flying 6,000 letters from Allahabad to Naini and back. Letters were delivered by air mail from Allahabad to Calcutta on February 22, 1911. Civil aviation continued to grow with the first Cairo-Karachi-Calcutta service being started in November 1918. Aviation continued to grow and the first flight from England to India by an Indian crew – R.N. Chawla and Aspy Engineer (later Air Marshal and Chief of the Air Staff, IAF) – was undertaken in August 1929. The legendary J.R.D. Tata was the first Indian pilot to fly solo (a DH-Moth) from India to England in May 3-12, 1930, while contesting the Agha Khan Race. Aspy Engineer had started the same race from England to India and finally won the race while J.R.D. Tata came second.

Tata Sons Ltd proposed a plan in 1929 to start a commercial service connecting Karachi-Bombay by air, but the British Indian government rejected the proposal though the era of domestic air transport had already begun. It was finally in October 1932 that the Tatas succeeded in starting operations of the Karachi-Ahmedabad-Bombay-Bellary-Madras service. A new company called the Indian Trans-Continental Airways was formed in May 1933, in which the Imperial Airways (based in London) held a 51 percent share and the government in New Delhi held a 24 percent share to operate on the Karachi-Singapore and Karachi-Calcutta sectors. In 1933, Tata Air Lines (which would become Air India later on, in 1946, and become the national flag carrier abroad after independence) was followed by Indian National Airways based in Delhi, with a service connecting Calcutta and Rangoon besides one connecting Calcutta-Dacca (now Dhaka, capital of Bangladesh). These two airlines were followed by a third, Air Services of India, set up in 1937 to connect Bombay with some of the princely states in Kathiawar and Bombay-Kohlapur in the southeast, essentially as a passenger service. After 1946, a rash of airlines started to function across India. Even before the end of World War II, the Director of Civil Aviation worked out a development and expansion plan for civil aviation not too dissimilar to the "open skies" policy of later years.

Immediately after the war, there was a sudden boom in the civil airlines business. War surplus Dakotas were available from the Disposals at as low a price as Rs. 20,000 per aircraft, and spare parts were also available in abundance at very low prices. On the eve of independence, 21 airline companies were registered to operate on 122 routes. Ultimately, the government granted provisional licences to 11 companies that included the already operating four companies and new ones like Deccan Airways, Dalmia Jain Airways, Bharat Airways, Airways (India), Orient Airways, Mistri Airways, Ambica Airways and Jupiter Airways. Nearly 200 Dakotas had been purchased and commissioned into service (although 30-40 would have been enough) by these airlines and, hence, the average rate of utilisation per aircraft dropped to a mere 500 hours per year as compared to the 1,700 hours assumed in the original plan. But the overall load factor during 1947-49 was much above 65 percent and well above the international load factor.[1] Independence and partition did not seriously impact the airline business except that a number of non-scheduled operated ones joined the list of airlines. Kalinga Airlines stands out among these airlines and undertook yeoman service even through the 1962 Sino-Indian War in air maintenance of the civil and military population in today's Arunachal Pradesh.

The large scale requirement of the civil airlines, along with the needs of the Indian Air Force for transport aircraft, raises the basic question that is central to our present study: *why did India not go in for design and manufacture of transport aircraft* leave alone the needs of general aviation in spite of an aircraft factory having been established as early as 1940?

Hindustan Aircraft Ltd

The establishment of an aircraft factory as early as 1940 makes a story of its own, though not surprising, given that a large number of emerging Indian entrepreneurs like the Tatas, Birlas, etc. had started after World War I to set up industrial enterprises, though at a small scale, succeeding only when the British Government of India was willing to allow it. It is in this context that a lesser known industrialist, who had concentrated on sugarcane production and associated industry in today's Maharashtra, Walchand Hirachand decided to set up an automotive factory, but landed up establishing an aircraft factory in 1940. It remains the only aircraft factory in India, roping in major areas of aircraft production with small ancillary entities across the country.

Hindustan Aircraft Ltd, as the company came to be called, began as an Indo-American private joint venture that came about through a chance meeting during a transcontinental flight. What happened was that Walchand was travelling from America (where he had gone to explore the possibility of establishing an automobile plant in India) back to India in the autumn of 1939 when he met Mr. William Douglas Pawley, Chairman of Inter-Continent Corporation and a Director of Harlow Aircraft Company in California who was on his way to Hong Kong in the same aircraft. Pawley had already set up a number of aircraft factories in China and Walchand invited him to come to India to help set up an aircraft factory. Pawley showed confidence that this could be done, India's backwardness in industry notwithstanding, if government support was forthcoming. This might have posed a serious roadblock since New Delhi had turned down the Tatas' 1929 proposal to start an airline. However, with the war clouds almost bursting over Europe, and Britain in serious economic and industrial difficulties, things were perhaps different now.

By the time the two industrialists landed in Hong Kong, they had refined their proposal. Further on, after landing at Manila, Walchand, based on the discussions with Pawley, sent a telegram to the Commander-in-Chief (C-in-C) in New Delhi with a fairly firm proposal, offering to set up an aircraft factory to build military fighters and bomber aeroplanes "to your specifications in cooperation with well-known American manufacturers acceptable to you with their guarantee of performance by an Indian-owned Company."[2] The telegram went on to offer a schedule of production and the terms of payment for aircraft purchased by the government. However, no reply was received, even after another telegram was sent a few days later from Hong Kong; and yet another telegram was repeated from Singapore later. On reaching Bombay, Walchand sent his fifth cable to which there was some response, though not from the C-in-C, but from the Government of India's Commerce Member, Sir A. Ramaswamy Mudliar who agreed to discuss the issues raised by Walchand when he met the former in Bombay. But for months, there was no progress in spite of the fact that the British, by now hard pressed by the German defeat of France and fearing an imminent invasion of Britain, were now in a disastrous situation. The British government clearly instructed its government in New Delhi regarding defence equipment supplies from the homeland: "Make your own arrangements for defence, especially in the air."[3]

The government was finally convinced by June 1940 that starting an aircraft manufacturing project in India would be a viable project though it would face many difficulties in the process. After all, in a country devoid of industrial capacity except in a few areas like textiles, the supporting manufacturing capacity did not exist. The essential plant and machinery would have to be imported as would raw material, and even qualified technical personnel would have to be brought in from outside. On the other hand, if China could set up a number of aircraft industries, including three by William Pawley alone, it was possible to run one in India. The telegram from Walchand and Pawley also emphasised that the Western manufacturers producing aircraft in those days were not entirely self-sufficient as regards raw material and other needs. But Walchand and his partners had not been sitting idle since the first telegram, sent nearly a year earlier.

Starting on May 10, 1940, Walchand had hired an 8-seater Dragon Rapide to undertake reconnaissance to select the site for the proposed aircraft factory. After a six-day survey of the general area of present-day Karnataka, the planners zeroed in on the area close to five lakes on the eastern edge of Bangalore (now Bengaluru) Cantonment area. On the other hand, the Government of India suddenly started to show interest in the proposal. Walchand went up to Simla, the summer capital of India, where he held wide ranging discussions with officials, arguing his case especially with the Supply Department. He made it clear that if explicit information was available on "how many planes were

required, of what types and within what period, what advance
could be paid on the selling price, how much and what kind
of help of a general nature was forthcoming, then we can
get on with the job."4 Lord Linlithgow, the Viceroy of India,
and members of his Executive Council decided to discuss
the proposal and guarantee support to Walchand's project.
Walchand immediately asked Pawley to return to India with
outline plans, along with his chief technician.

On July 1, 1940, they all went up to Simla and serious
discussions with the Chief of Supply of the Government of India
took place, and within a miraculous 72 hours, the Government
of India's decision to establish an aircraft factory in India was
finalised. A provisional agreement between the two sides was
concluded on July 4, 1940. The government gave its approval
in principle to the proposal of Walchand Hirachand and his
associates on December 16, 1940. This was soon followed
by the registration of the factory in Mysore under the name
of Hindustan Aircraft Limited company under the Mysore
Companies Act on December 23, 1940. The foundation stone
was laid on January 12, 1941, and work to build India's first
aircraft factory, now a behemoth, was started on a 2,100 acre
site, of which the Maharaja of Mysore gave 700 acres free of
cost (besides other concessions) and also invested Rs. 25 lakh in
shares. In return, he was made a member of the Board; and the
Government of India also invested an equal amount in shares
with a seat on the Board of Directors. William Douglas Pawley
was appointed the President of the Board and the Walchand
Hirachand Group became the Managing Agents of the company.
Rapid progress was made in setting up the company and within
three months most of the machinery and more than half of the
(22) technicians being imported from America had arrived at
Bangalore.

The task set for the company at the beginning was to assemble and later manufacture Harlow PC-5 trainers, Curtiss Hawk fighters and Vultee attack bombers. The first orders placed on HAL included:[5]

20 Harlow PC-5 trainers to be delivered in the first seven months under Project 156.

48 Curtiss 75A-SP Hawk fighters to be delivered by July 31, 1942.

74 Vultee V-12-D attack bombers.

The first aircraft assembled at HAL, a Harlow trainer, flew within eight months of the company's registration and was exported to China for its air force as were the following few aircraft as part of Pawley's previous commitments. Production of Harlow PC-5 trainers and Curtiss Hawk P-36 fighters then started. The factory also locally designed, built and flew the first ten-seater glider. The glider production did not proceed any further on questionable grounds except that it was a year ahead of the requirements of the "Wingate Raiders" brigade which was inserted inside Japanese-held Burma from towed gliders. While presiding over the first anniversary celebrations of HAL, General Manager McCarty observed that phenomenal progress in aircraft manufacturing had taken place. This, he said, was achieved through the sustained effort, hardship and sacrifices of the HAL employees. He went on to state, "Aircraft manufacturing is the most complex industrial enterprise in the modern world. A modern bomber, such as the one that was being produced at the initial stage, had more than 200,000 parts."[6] Even in America, with a fully established aircraft industry, this would have been a very difficult undertaking. McCarty added, "We are actually manufacturing today, from raw materials, unlike a factory in America, where accessories, castings, difficult machine parts and sub-assemblies are usually obtained from sub-contractors."

Looking at the rapid progress made to establish the aircraft factory and begin a robust programme of manufacture, the Government of India decided to become a shareholder, buying Rs. 25 lakh worth of shares. However, it nominated an unduly large number of government officials (Air Marshal Sir John Higgins, Financial Adviser E.T. Coates and Secretary to the Supply Department E.M. Jenkins) to the Board. This reorganisation brought in official support; but it also made HAL subject to the colonial interests which, at best, had discouraged industrialisation in India. The Japanese attack on Pearl Harbour on December 7, 1941, created a new situation east of India, especially for the British Empire. The disastrous defeat of the British in Southeast Asia created further concerns about the threat to India. The cruise of the Japanese fleet along the eastern coast of India, dropping bombs at Madras (where the Governor issued instructions to evacuate the city), Vijayawada, Kakinada and all the way north to Calcutta, created utter panic in the British Government of India since there were virtually no military forces south of the Vindhyas. But after this display of power, the Japanese went away to the Pacific Ocean, merely leaving a small garrison at the Andaman and Car Nicobar groups of islands. But the British fear lingered on.

Pushpinder Singh writes that the Government of India even contemplated adopting the "scorched earth" strategy, and Jenkins "suggested to Walchand that if Japanese parachutists were dropped in India, or landed in Madras, a mere 200 miles away, they would certainly head for Bangalore first; the Government thought it advisable to make contingency plans to destroy the Hindustan Aircraft Company so as to prevent it from Japanese exploitation."[7] When Walchand disagreed, the government then suggested that Walchand and the Mysore government sell off their share in the company as, with the plant and considerable equipment coming from America, the work was to be on a "no profit" basis under the British-US lend lease agreement. Surely the Americans could have been persuaded to allow continuation of Hindustan Aircraft Ltd as an Indian-American private joint venture and treated the factory on the same terms as American companies that converted from civil to military production; and this could hardly have been on no-profit basis. The contradiction in the two positions is obvious as is the British guile in taking over the factory. Along with the idea of a threat of Japanese bombing of HAL, Walchand and his associates thought it prudent to cut their losses, and accept the compensation offered by the government. The Maharaja of Mysore refused to sell his shares, but agreed not to have any management role during the war and for a year or so after. This was not honoured by the British government after the war. Thus, HAL came fully under government ownership and control from March 1942. By December 1942, control of HAL was transferred to the 10th USAAF for the duration of the war, which, understandably, considered overhaul more important for their immediate requirements than assembly of aircraft. Hence, the assembly programme at HAL was suspended by mid-1943 and for the next two years, HAL, the factory to manufacture aircraft, regressed to become a large size repair and overhaul workshop!

Could the requirements of the war have been fulfilled in any better way? The answer is obviously yes. Since the technical work in overhauling aircraft and engines is well below that which is required to manufacture these from raw materials up (what HAL had begun to do), a simple expansion of semi-skilled and unskilled manpower should have served the needs of the USAAF, especially when the supervisory work was handled by American technicians and engineers. Perhaps a maximum of two hangars might have been needed in addition to what the USAAF needed. Hence, the earlier plan of assembly and manufacture of at least three types of aircraft could have continued. HAL employed a total of 14,000 persons and only a fraction of this number would have sufficed for design and development work. As it is, over 1,000 combat aircraft had been overhauled in HAL while it was under USAAF control, and assembly of fighters and bombers should not have posed any difficulties, especially of the types being overhauled. On the other hand, what India had to offer through its aircraft factory was reduced dependence on England for supplies (which, because of the war conditions and the distances involved, had become a serious problem) and a ready-made hub for assembly and manufacture of frontline aircraft could have been undertaken in India for the Allied war effort. But, as had happened often, the imperial goals probably remained uppermost in the minds of the colonial rulers in New Delhi.

The net effect was that while we may feel proud of the number of engines and aircraft overhauled at HAL for the USAAF, HAL's autonomous capacity as a rapidly emerging modern Indian aircraft factory was nipped in the bud. The history of HAL, the premier aircraft factory of the country, after the end of World War II in August 1945 till August 15, 1947, when India became independent, can be related in a few sentences. When the USAAF handed back HAL, it had over 13,000 personnel who were rapidly retrenched to around 3,000. During the three years that HAL was under the Americans for maintenance and overhaul of aircraft and aero-engines, it overhauled 3,312 aero-engines (an average of three/day) and 1,004 aircraft (an average of one per day). By any logic, this was an outstanding performance and ideally suitable as a foundation on which to build the Indian aircraft industry. HAL had even successfully converted many B-24 Liberator bombers to C-27 tanker aircraft during the war.

But before we proceed further, there is also the story of another aircraft factory to be told. J.R.D. Tata, himself a pilot who stood second in the first London-Karachi air race in 1930, had great aspirations toward unlimited aviation activity in India. His vision included manufacture of aircraft, besides the airline which he had already set up and other allied operations. JRD sent Nevill Vintcent to the United States in mid-1941 to explore the possibility of association with some American manufacturer for co-production of their aircraft in India. But after extensive search, Vintcent found that all avenues had already been closed, essentially as a fall-out of the US-UK "lend-lease" agreement and the decision of the US Administration that all surplus production capacity was to be allotted to the Allied war effort. Vintcent then left for London to negotiate with the UK Minister of Aircraft Production a contract to build and equip an aircraft factory and manufacture any aircraft that would meet the requirements of the Air Forces in India.

Vintcent met Lord Beaverbrook and this mission proved successful, with the result of a promise of a contract for the provision of an aircraft factory in India to manufacture light training aircraft. To implement this idea, Tata Sons Ltd set up a subsidiary company called Tata Aircraft Ltd (in March 1942) with JRD as the Chairman and Vintcent as the Managing Director. An open area in Poona (now Pune) was selected as the site for the factory and recruitment of personnel as well as purchases of supplies from England was started through the Tatas' London agents. The concept was to build the twin-engined high speed and highly manoeuvrable de Havilland Mosquito fighter-bomber and reconnaissance aircraft. Unfortunately, the US-UK lend-lease agreement again came in the way and obviated the need to build trainers in India since they could be produced far more easily and faster in the US, Canada and England. This hit both HAL and Tata Aircraft adversely. JRD Tata explained:[8]

> My devotion to aviation was not only to the airline but to aviation and aeroplanes. So when the war came along, with the help of Nevill Vintcent, we decided to offer to build up an aircraft industry that would be useful after the war. So what should we build? Metal aeroplanes needed a lot of metallurgical materials and experience we couldn't import easily, so we decided to offer to build the Mosquito — a light, twin-engined fighter bomber. It was made of wood and could go extremely fast. The de Havilland company built it and it was designed to carry one big bomb. It was used to bomb Berlin. We would have to import the engine, of course. The body was a fairly simple structure, very successful. The British Government said 'yes,' and we began to build a factory in Poona near the Aga Khan Palace.

Vintcent was sent back to England to get the contract. While preparations were being made to establish the factory and install the machinery, the British government cancelled the order. Tata regretfully felt, *"I think it was purely that they didn't want India to make a good aeroplane to compete with the British, so they killed it.* Had we started with the Mosquito, we would have gone on to other aeroplanes" (emphasis added). It may be recalled that the Allies had encouraged private enterprises to set up aircraft factories in China where the Sino-Japanese War was going on; and Pawley alone had three factories going there. But there was an unexplained resistance to the development of an aircraft industry even under government control in India which, barring the Japanese incursion into India on its Burma border in Akyab-Imphal-Kohima in early 1944, was peaceful. At the same time, India's contribution to the British was enormous. It may be recalled that India had provided 2.6 million troops (historically, the largest volunteer force engaged in the war). There also grew an opinion in government circles that the Mosquito, with its plywood structure, would not be able to withstand the Indian climate of rains and humidity, not that the English weather was dry by any standards. But within a few years (when India was on the eve of independence), British experts were arguing that the de Havilland (the factory that had manufactured the Mosquito) manufactured Vampire with a wooden fuselage was the most suitable aircraft for the Indian Air Force!

Vintcent did manage to get a contract for the *Horsa* troop-carrying gliders and engaged personnel, purchased material, etc. with the assistance of the Tatas' agents in London for the manufacture of the *Horsa*. Unfortunately, he died when his aircraft was lost, without a trace, on the way back. JRD met the Viceroy and extracted a promise that the Government of India's Supply Department would take over the responsibility for the contract for the *Horsa* glider which the British Ministry of Aircraft Production had given to Tata Aircraft Ltd and a new contract was drawn up. But London asked the Tatas to switch to *Invasion* gliders which in JRD's opinion would not be workable since New Delhi could not answer the question of where these gliders would be used and how they would be transported to such places. Meanwhile, the Burma front required an accelerated war effort and led to different priorities. The German submarine threat had been reduced to manageable levels to provide for a degree of transportation between England and India. Fighter aircraft were arriving by sea at Bombay and required skilled manpower to assemble them and the task was taken over by Tata Aircraft after the glider contract was cancelled by the Government of India. In addition, the Santa Cruz (Bombay) based Air Works also participated in the assembly and support activities of imported aircraft.

Thus, the two unique and landmark initiatives taken by private Indian businessmen (and supported by the Mysore state government in the case of HAL) to manufacture state-of-the-art aircraft were relegated to aircraft servicing, essentially due to the British pursuit of imperial interests. The manpower of HAL was rapidly reduced from 14,000 Indian employees to 3,000 and the 250 US civilian experts and 600 USAAF experts returned to the United States. No effort was made to design and develop an aircraft till independence in spite of excellent facilities and the large number of technicians available.

British Technical Mission

After the control of HAL reverted to the Government of India in December 1945, the government invited a Technical Mission from the UK to review, and advise on, the potential and practical possibility of organising an aircraft industry in India. Such an industry was expected to support not only the increasing requirement of the Indian Air Force, but also the needs of civil aviation which was to rapidly increase to 11 airlines. The mission commenced its work in India in March 1946, visiting HAL and other industrial establishments in the country. A month later, it submitted its report, which stated:[9]

> Of the three factories considered, HAL at Bangalore is the only one
> still working as a producer of aeronautical material on a reasonable
> scale. It has the largest experience of aircraft work ..... Hindustan
> Aircraft is the only factory in which the whole process of building an
> aircraft from semi-finished material has been attempted.

Further, the report stated:

> The physical assets of this company are equal to, or better than, those
> at both Barrackpore (which mainly manufactured small arms for the
> Army at Ishapore) and Poona. When the potential of Bangalore is
> exhausted, another source should be introduced, parallel with HAL.
> Strategically, Bangalore is the only site which complies with the
> specifications of the Air and General Staff. Transport by road and rail
> is satisfactory. Bangalore has a unique advantage of its proximity to
> large centres of learning like the Indian Institute of Science, Central
> College, Engineering College, Occupational Institute, etc. The wide
> enthusiasm and interest on the part of the Government of India and
> people of Mysore are assets. The existence at HAL of a wider range
> of engineering facilities, including a good foundry and chemical
> laboratory, are of considerable importance.

The mission's report recommended that HAL must
obtain "reasonable" orders for aircraft, both from the military
and civilian customers, the latter being universally "a by-
product." On the basis of the mission's recommendations, the
Government of India decided to establish a nationalised aircraft
industry in the country, giving a 20-year target for "complete
self-sufficiency." This target date expired in 1966 by which
time HAL had almost completely abdicated its responsibilities
for self-sufficiency in design and development of aircraft which
is the critical foundation of even self-reliance, leave alone such
self-sufficiency.

Independence, Defence and Partition

India finally achieved independence from the British rule

on August 15, 1947. But the British were leaving behind a deindustrialised country wherein they had been unwilling to introduce the benefits of the Industrial Revolution nearly two centuries after it had erupted in England and rapidly expanded to the European nations and peoples. India merely produced small arms and ammunition through makeshift arrangements (like using the railway workshop to produce machine grenades and shells) during a five-year World War; but its total production of even such items of war was far below that of other British colonies inhabited by British settlers, like Australia and South Africa![10] By its misguided policies of imperialism, Britain hastened its own economic and industrial decline.

Given the poor state of economic conditions, the economy itself being dependent on agriculture and related services, and the pathetic state of industrialisation in the country, it is obvious that the defence industry would be of hardly any significance. That this was so nearly five years after the Japanese were thrown out from India clearly indicates the unwillingness or inability of the colonial government to establish a defence industry in any meaningful way. What was obvious by the end of World War II was that even from the British perspective, the "British empire was collapsing, and not even a dramatic expansion of India's defence capabilities could save it."[11] Even the production and infrastructure for small arms and their ammunition that was being produced during the war was wound down (see Appendix A for details). As may be seen, the fledgling defence industry employed nearly 120,000 workers in 1945. Of the 15 ordnance factories, five were closed down before 1947 and the number of workers came down to a paltry 15,000 or so. A degree of drawdown after the war was inevitable. But it seems that even by early 1948 when the war in J&K was at its peak — in fact, the longest war that the Indian armed forces have fought after World War II — and Hyderabad was showing signs of raising its armed militias (Razakars) to subdue the non-Muslim majority population of this strategically important state, the capacity of small arms production had been reduced remarkably. As may be seen, in all, 15 ordnance factories were functioning in early 1945 — a tremendous growth since 1942 when the war came to the Indian frontiers. By early 1948, with the Pakistan Army entrenched in J&K and a severe war going on, these had been reduced to 10 factories, with output reduced to a fraction of the earlier years.

In the absence of viable ordnance factories, reliance was placed during World War II on 14 railway workshops across the country to produce shells and undertake other ancillary tasks of machining and forging shells, grenades and mortar bombs, besides manufacturing 6 lb shots. These had continued to carry out their original tasks for the railways during the war, and after the war was over, they reverted fully to the tasks of repair and overhaul of railway equipment.

During World War II, India did not produce any aircraft while its aircraft factory, HAL, was tasked to overhaul aircraft and aero-engines for the USAAF (covered in detail in a later chapter). An overwhelming majority of vehicles and automotives was of North American origin since Britain itself had not been able to supply them. Some of the chassis were used for building armoured vehicles in India for the war in Burma. The Indian Army, which had grown to around 2.6 million troops, was demobilised after World War II, and after the partition in 1947, was left with a total of 276,369 troops.

Partition of Military Forces and Assets
It is in this context that the partition of India also resulted in

a further setback to the Indian military capability and defence industry in particular. The partition of military assets and defence industry added to India's military weaknesses and vulnerability. The basic formula adopted for the division of military forces and assets between India and Pakistan was in the ratio of 70:30 on the basis of the overall population of the subcontinent, on the assumption of 30 percent being Muslim and others being non-Muslim. But it should have been clear to everyone that all Muslims, especially those in large concentrations (like in UP) and those who had little cultural and linguistic empathy with the languages of the emerging Pakistan, would stay back in their ancestral homes and professions in most of India. The fact that a large number of Muslim leaders were to stay in India in eminent positions also added to that factor. Hence, a near majority of the Muslim population of erstwhile India was unlikely to go to Pakistan (the actual ratio of Muslims in India and Pakistan after partition was closer to 86:14) and, hence, this formula weighed heavily against India's defence assets, with far higher proportion of arms and equipment allotted to Pakistan than what the partition logic would have dictated, in the process, making Pakistan militarily much stronger. Ironically, it is the Pakistanis who have been complaining that they did not receive their right share of the division of the military and its assets and continue to hold this grievance till today.

A Joint Defence Council was headed by General Sir Claude Auchinleck, the erstwhile Commander-in-Chief, but the division of the military and its assets must be judged in the context of two crucial factors: (a) Pakistan had launched an unprovoked war against J&K in September 1947, and the ruler, finding it difficult to stop the Pakistani military-led tribal/guerrilla forces, acceded to India on October 26. Hence, from October 27, 1947, India had to defend the territory now part of India, while the division of military assets was to be completed by June 1948; and (b) Hyderabad, the largest state in Central India, with over 85 percent non-Muslims ruled by a Muslim ruler had opted to stay independent (and remained so till September 1948). The ruler imported arms and ammunition from Karachi, the capital of Pakistan, no doubt authorised by the Pakistan government and army, through clandestine supplies air delivered by the British/Australians like Sydney Cotton, to raise a large military/militia armed force named Razakars to control the majority non-Muslim population. Under these circumstances, it would have been unrealistic (and against its own interests) for India to have continued to transfer arms and supplies to the Pakistan Army and Hyderabad's hostile forces to fight the Indian Army. Even then, the aircraft and naval vessels required to be transferred to Pakistan for its air force were completed by mid-November 1947 although Auchinleck believed that "the partition of the RIAF (Royal Indian Air Force) into two forces .... will lead to the disintegration of the RIAF as it now exists, to an extent which will leave India well-nigh defenceless against air attack for a period of years which cannot be estimated."[12]

What little defence industry existed in the pre-partition days had been located in the Gangetic plains and peninsular India in order to keep it deeper inside India's strategic depth, away from a potential German attack from the northwest and a Japanese attack from the east. Hence, few (beyond the Karachi shipyard and aircraft maintenance depot, etc.), actually fell in the territory that became Pakistan. Shifting industry was an impractical proposition but could well have been done if Pakistan had not started the war with India. However, India agreed on December 1, 1947 (nearly three months after the war was launched by Pakistan) to provide Rs. 60 million to Pakistan

to create defence industries! Pakistan used this money, along
with its other funds in 1948 (while waging the war against
India), to order nearly Pounds 2.66 million worth of small
arms and light vehicles, the bulk of the orders being placed
on Canada.[13] By May 1949, Italy had become Pakistan's major
source of small arms, explosives, and heavy calibre guns. Poland
supplied 40 million rounds of small arms ammunition, 20,000
rifles and 3,000 machine-guns to Pakistan. Czechoslovakia sent
53,000 rifles for $4.5 million. One interesting Pakistani deal
for arms in December 1947 (generally assumed to be for the
tribals who had already been given 4,000 rifles from Pakistan's
existing stocks)[14] was for a rather limited quantity of 600 .303
rifles, 250 tommy guns, and 20,000 hand grenades concluded
by Pakistani officials with private dealers rather than the
normal acquisition from government sources, and was more
likely to have been for supply to the Razakars in Hyderabad to
maintain deniability.

At the same time, it needs to be noted that all the supply
depots of the pre-independence Indian military were located
at Lahore, Nowshera, Bannu, Quetta, Karachi and Bombay
since the bulk of the Army and Air Force was deployed in
West Punjab and Northwest Frontier Province (NWFP). With
partition, these supply depots (with the exception of Bombay)
fell in the area that became Pakistan and, thus, Pakistan
received enormous quantities of stores and supplies meant
actually for the whole Indian Army.

The Indian Air Force had dropped down to six combat
squadrons against the nine before independence. In order to
make up the deficiency in the force structure, India requested
Britain in November 1947 for the sale of over 100 aircraft (52
Tempest II fighter-bombers, some jet fighters, one twin-engine
photo-reconnaissance aircraft and an unspecified number of

twin-engines bombers, 12 Dove communications aircraft, and 60 Spitfire XVIII trainers, and seven naval vessels) for delivery by March 1948.[15] Britain was willing since it helped to use blocked sterling funds, but suddenly found there was no aircraft in stock in Britain! The only supply source was the British air base at Mauripur in Karachi. But Pakistani authorities, having learnt of this deal, promptly impounded them and raised their own demand for 34 tropicalised Tempest aircraft in January 1948. Meanwhile, Australia decided on January 13, 1948, to prohibit sale of arms to India and Pakistan and the United States followed suit on March 11, on the grounds that this would escalate the conflict in Kashmir. It may be recalled that Pakistan was insisting even at the UN Security Council till July 1948 that its military was not involved in the Kashmir war! Hence, the argument of escalation was quite fallacious. The reality is that the Cold War had already set in and Britain had persuaded its allies (including the US, which initially accepted J&K's accession to India) that Pakistan needed to be supported. More important for our present study is the fact that the Indian armed forces possessed obsolete weapons, there was hardly any defence industry worth the mention in India which had a long way to go before recovering from the deindustrialisation of the previous two centuries, and the population was mired in poverty. Hence, while fighting the aggressor was essential, no elected democratic government could afford not to pay serious attention to steps to alleviate and remove poverty. And in the context of the times, access to technology and creating an industrial base became critical.

Appendix A

Principal Indian Munitions Factories

The figures below are for monthly production in early 1945 and early 1948 respectively, unless otherwise stated. The number of workers employed is shown where the information is available.

Location	War-time Production Early 1945	Peace-time Production Early 1948
Kirkee (near Poona)	Small-arms ammunition, 26 million rounds;[a] 3.7" 25-lb. shells, 200,000;[b] grenades, 115,000.[b] 15,000 workers.	Small-arms ammunition, 1.5 million rounds; shells, 5,000; mortar shells, 4,000. 2,300 workers.
Ambernath (near Bombay)	25-lb.brass shell cases, 70,000-160,000; 3.7"anti-aircraft shells, 3,000 workers.	25-lb. shell cases, 1,500. 1,000 workers.
Katni (near Jabalpur)	Small-arms ammunition components (for filling at Kirkee).[c]	Driving bands for high-explosive shells, 4,300;[d] Brass, 106 short tons.
Khamaria (near Jabalpur)	Small-arms ammunition; ammunition filling; pyrotechnics.[c]	Closed September 1946.
Jabalpur	Gun carriages. [c]	Gun carriage repair.[c]
Muradnagar (near Meerut)	Moulded steel 250-lb. aerial bomb bodies, 5,000; hand grenades, 50,000; mortar shells, 50, 000. 5,000 workers.	Mortar shell bodies, 2,000. 1,400 workers.
Kanpur	25-lb. shells, 15,000; 3.7" shells, 45,000; 25-lb. shell gun assemblies.[c]	25-lb shells, 1,500; 3.7" shells 24,000; 9,000 mortar shells.
Ishapore-Metal and Steel (near Calcutta)	Non-ferrous metals; ammunition cups and cases; steel; shell forgings; steel billets for small-arms manufacture, gun castings.[c]	25-lb. shell forgings, 4,000; rifle barrel billets, 5,000; special steel for arms production, 126 tons; (40 steel and non-ferrous metal products for railroads and industry).

Ishapore-Rifle (near Calcutta)	Rifles, 16,000; bayonets;[e] Vickers light machine-guns.[c] 23, 000 workers.	Rifles, 750; rifle repair, 2,000; 3,000 workers.
Cossipore (near Calcutta)	3.7" howitzers, 32; 25-lb. shells, 48,000; 3.7" howitzer shells, 36, 000; smoke shells, 17, 000; shell fuses, 100,000. 17,000 workers.	25-lb. shells, 2,000; primers and fuses (c). 3, 000 workers.
Dum Dum (near Calcutta)	Gas masks, 32, 000; Bren-gun tripods, 300.	Closed.
Lucknow	Fuses and primers for all types of shell, mines, and grenades.	Closed. Main building used by East Indian Railways.
Hyderabad (Deccan)	Began production in August 1945 with monthly capacity of 3,000 Bren-guns.	Closed February 1947. Total production less than 500. Sold to private concern.
Amritsar	Shell components and cases.[c]	Metal products for railways and private industry.
Dehra Dun	Binoculars, telescopic sights, clinometers, compasses.[f]	Binoculars, 210; clinometers, 17; prismatic compasses, 120.

Notes

a. December 1943.
b. June 1944.
c. No figures are available.
d. January 1947.
e. No monthly figures are available. The Ishapore rifle factory produced 214,000 bayonets during 1944-45.
f. No exact figures are available. According to the Planning and Operations Division of the US Army Department, the optical-instrument factory at Dehra Dun produced a "major part" of the 20,000 binoculars, 1,262 telescopic sights, 1,805 clinometers, and 35,457 compasses manufactured in India during World War II.

Source: Adapted from "Strategic Intelligence Digest: India: Economic," October 1, 1948, Department of the Army, NAR, P&O 350.05 FW 178/85, 119-121.

Appendix B

Railway Workshops
(Munitions items produced during World War II)

Railway Company	Site	Major Products
Bengal and Assam	Kanchrapara	Shell and grenade machining
Bombay, Baroda, and Central India	Amjer	Shell and mortar bomb forging and machining
Bombay, Baroda, and Central India	Lower Parel	Shells
Bengal-Nagpur	Nagpur	Shot
Bengal-Nagpur	Kharagpur	Shell and grenade machining
East Indian	Jamalpur	Shell forging
East Indian	Tatanagar	Armoured vehicles
Great Indian Peninsula	Matunga (I)	Shell and mortar bomb forging and machining
Great Indian Peninsula	Matunga (II)	Field equipment
Madras and Southern Mahratta	Arkonam	Field equipment
Madras and Southern Mahratta	Perambur (near Madras)	Shell and grenade machining
North-Western	Moghalpura (near Lahore)	Shell and grenade machining
South Indian	Golden Rock	6 lb. shot
South Indian	Trichinopoly	Aircraft parts

Source: Adapted from "Strategic Intelligence Digest: India: Economic," October 1, 1948, Department of the Army, NAR, P&O 350.05 FW 178/85, 119-21, 122. All workshops continued to undertake work for the railways and after the war, reverted to their basic role in the railways. It is obvious that there were more railway workshops like those in Karachi and Rawalpindi, etc. (now in Pakistan) belonging to Northern Railways which are not listed here but, no doubt, were tasked to assist in defence production processes during World War II.

Notes

1. M.R. Dhekney, Air *Transport in India: Growth and Problems* (Bombay: Vora & Co Publishers Ltd, 1953), p. 87.
2. Pushpinder Singh, *Diamonds in the Sky; Sixty Years of HAL 1940-2001* (New Delhi: The Society for Aerospace Studies, 2001), p. 21.
3. Ibid., p. 22.
4. Ibid., p. 22.
5. Ibid., p. 26.
6. Alka Sen, *Glimpses into Indian Aviation 1910-1997* (Bombay: Indian Aviation News Services Ltd., 1998), p. 416.
7. Singh, n. 2, p. 29.
8. Sen, n. 6, p. 435.
9. Singh, n. 2, p. 35
10. A. Martin Wainwright, *Inheritance of Empire: Britain, India, and the Balance of Power in Asia, 1938-55* (Westport: Praeger, 1994).
11. Ibid., p. 24.
12 Cited in "Reorganisation of the Army and Air Forces in India, 1945: Report of a Committee Set up by His Excellency the Commander-in-Chief in India," Appendix C, normally referred to as the *Willcox Report*.
13. Pakistan Joint Consultative Committee, Note of Discussion Held at the Treasury, November 29, 1948, PRO, T 225/353.
14. See Major General Akbar Khan (who planned and led the 1947-48 War), *Raiders in Kashmir* (Delhi: Army Publishers).
15. Wainwright, n. 10, p. 91.

3

The Quest for Technology

A country which is economically strong, which is industrially developed, is much more in a position to defend itself than any other country, however brave its people might be. The great countries today, from the point of view of military power or defence, are countries which have developed industrially, which have developed in the exploration of science and its progeny. Therefore, the obvious course for us to follow, we thought of it after independence, was *to build our country up industrially and bring about in fact that long deferred industrial revolution in this country.*

— Jawaharlal Nehru[1]

India's quest for technology after independence must be seen in the context of its philosophy for foreign and security policies which came to be given the name "non-alignment" much after it had been put into practice. It was inevitable that this policy of seeking "strategic autonomy" in a comprehensive framework would bring its own benefits and costs. In hindsight, it is clear that the benefits have been far greater than the costs in spite of the latter, including the anti-India policies of the United States during the past six-odd decades. The most adverse consequence in this context, in fact, has been the problem of India's access to technology, not only in relation to defence but also to the civil sector which was brought under the ambit of technology denial regimes under the rubric of "dual technology." As seen in the earlier chapters, India faced a major challenge even to feed its rapidly growing population, leave alone building a technology base for defence. And the technology denial regime practised by the Western powers for decades only tended to retard the process of India's reindustrialisation.

"Building a Self-Reliant Industrial System"

Our main interest in the complex growth of India, its successes and failures, over the past six and more decades is the growth of science and technology in general and defence industry in particular so that we can look closely at our past experiences in the aircraft industry and evolve suitable policy options for the future. The past is important, therefore, to provide the context without whose understanding we could make errors of judgement about the future options based on assumptions that may not be sustainable. Two fundamental/overriding factors must be kept in mind when examining the past and thinking about the future. These arise out of the basic logic of independence. Mahatma Gandhi wrote a brief letter to Jawaharlal Nehru in 1938 expressing his view that independence was round the corner and, hence, "We must think of our foreign policy." This led to a series of formal and informal discussions among the leadership of the Indian National Congress and finally the All India Congress Committee adopted a resolution at its session in Haripur in 1939 laying down the principles of India's foreign policy that still hold good seven decades later: "India was resolved to maintain friendly and cooperative relations with all nations and avoid entanglements in military and similar alliances which tend to divide up the world into rival groups and thus endanger world peace."[2] This, in due course, would become the national policy and strategy of "non-alignment" and clearly not to be confused with NAM (Non-Aligned Movement) composed of the developing countries which had been mostly under colonial rule for nearly two centuries. Leaders like Jawaharlal Nehru had already been arguing against power politics which they held to be particularly menacing. With the impending demise of imperialism, Nehru visualised the opportunity for the emergence of an international framework that would allow stabilisation of conflict through maximising cooperation which was the only option in an age in which war had become as disastrous as it was, and national self-respect as universally demanding.[3]

The formal birth of the concept of non-alignment can be traced to the broadcast made by Jawaharlal Nehru (at that time the Vice-Chairman of the Viceroy's Executive Council in India) on September 7, 1946, indicating the response of a major nation about to emerge as an independent sovereign nation-state, when he stated:[4]

> We propose, as far as possible, to keep away from the power politics of groups, aligned against one another, which have led in the past to world wars and which may again lead to disasters on an even vaster scale.

Nehru also declared, "We shall take part in international conferences as a free nation with our own policy and not as a satellite of another nation."[5] If there was any hope of reducing the negative impact of the Cold War (which had started with all its negative consequences by the time India was acquiring its independence), especially for the developing countries, it lay in early prevention and a conceptual framework in which to pursue it. This conviction was strengthened by the emergence of Communist China on the international stage. India's early resistance to the great power conflict, in which China rapidly became a part through the Korean War, also provided a model for the newly emerging, but much weaker states of the post-colonial world. Nehru had declared in 1949, "It (freedom) consists fundamentally and basically of foreign relations. That is the test of independence. All else is local autonomy. Once foreign relations go out of our hands into the charge of somebody else, to that extent and in that measure, you are not independent."[6]

A more specific impetus and imperative of non-alignment for India was the problem of dealing with the aggressiveness of China which posed a challenge to India in comprehensive terms, besides the specific military terms, especially after it invaded and occupied Tibet by force. Two years after India's independence, Mao Zedong had called for the "brave Communist Party of India" to liberate the country.[7] Implicit in this call also was the concept of export of ideology. The Indian leadership, including Nehru, was conscious of this challenge.[8]

The important point here is that *the principle and strategy of non-alignment as a political philosophy would have to be accompanied by a defence policy of self-reliance.* This set the framework of the defence industry; and since there was little or no industry, leave alone defence industry (as shown in the previous two chapters), its broad parameters are best studied within what has been known as Nehru's Industrial-Technological Model for independent India. Based on actual policies and the articulated rationale for them, Baldev Raj Nayar has concluded that this model could be summed up as follows:[9]

> The basic point of departure for India in developing a model for industry and technology is that India is both an extremely poor, underdeveloped country as well as a country weak in defence capabilities while, at the same time, it is a major, potentially a great power. These two facts then determine the first order goals for the country, which are: first, India must raise the living standards of its population, and equally, second, India must provide for its national security as well as for a role in the world structure of power commensurate with its size and importance. At the second order level, the route to these major goals lies in the

accomplishment of rapid industrialisation in India. Consistent with the overall thrust of India's national goals in terms of national security, role, status in the world, and alleviation of poverty and improvement of living standards, India's industrial strategy ought to aim at the building of a self-reliant industrial system.

Even in hindsight, with a policy of non-alignment and self-reliance (the term self-sufficiency came to be used among the political bosses much later), it was clear that Britain and the European powers, not to talk of the Soviet Union and Japan, on the other side, would be more open to trade, technology access and weapons to India. And even the fact that the Cold War had started before India became independent, did not come in the way of India's access to technology and arms for its military forces during the first fifteen years and later. Even the US sold some equipment like the Fairchild C-119 Packet aircraft, Sikorsky S-55 helicopters, etc. during this period. It was also due to these factors that India had achieved significant self-reliance during the Nehru period.[10] But the real challenge continues to this day: import technology, or develop indigenous technology. Both contain their own challenges, at least some of which could be met only after the country began to record economic growth of around 8.5 percent per year on an average during the first decade of the 21st century. Even then, we risk what Dr. V Siddhartha had called the Technology-Triple-Trap:[11]

> The required 5D (Deterrence, Dissuasion, Denial, Disruption, Destruction) capabilities of the Armed Services foreseeable up to 2020 will call for appropriate provisioning of the Services with 5D "effects-based" technologies. But doing so by import will present insurmountable difficulties; for *what is developed abroad will not suit our requirements; what is suitable will be denied; what is not denied will be unaffordable.*
> This is the already recognizable *technology-triple-trap* that the Services are facing.

Fundamental Obstacles to Indian Industry

It may be recalled that the fundamental obstacle to the growth of modern industry in India was the colonial rule which coincided with the emergence of the Industrial Revolution which, in turn, facilitated the colonisation of India. The inevitable effect was prioritisation of the imperial interests in general, and the subjection of India to free trade after the 1813 proclamation abolishing the East India Company's trade monopoly in India, on one side, and the non-intervention by the state to promote industry in India, on the other, created deep handicaps to the development of an indigenous industry in India after independence.[12] It may be recalled that the *Indian Industrial Commission 1916-18* had emphasised the importance of "the work which will have to be done to place India on a firm basis of economic self-sufficiency and of self-defence."[13] In the process, the commission had clearly laid great emphasis on the *relationship of industry to defence and security*. But, as noted in the last chapter, nothing of consequence happened in the post-war period in the implementation of the recommendations of the commission.

The impact of the two World Wars did have some positive effect on industrialisation in India. But it came about more through an indirect route of discriminatory tariff policies than any positive policy from among the large number recommended by various commissions. The impact of World War II was limited largely by the single most important weakness of Indian industry: the lack of a capital goods base. Factory production even after the war hardly amounted to 6 percent of the national income. In 1947, electricity consumption was a mere 9.5 kwh per capita. Employment in the manufacturing sector actually reduced and even in 1951 (at 9.1 percent) was below the level (10 percent) of 1901, with the population virtually at the same level. In terms of details, the most important weakness of Indian industry at the time of independence was the lack of a capital goods base. Secondly, industry occupied a minor proportion of the total economy which itself was extremely weak and dependent on rain-fed agriculture since the canal-irrigated lands were lost to Pakistan. The consequence of the two was a poverty-stricken population. This is when Pakistan launched a war against India in J&K. At the same time, consolidation of the Indian state had to be undertaken and this led to a series of reorganisations of internal state boundaries to finally bring about a more coherent country within a federal structure.

When it came to acquiring science and technology for the future, India was faced with a series of choices it had to make: between investments in agriculture and/or industrialisation and if so, where should it focus its limited resources? Industrialisation raised many options, with different consequences. Countries like Germany, Japan and Italy were being rebuilt with the help of the Marshall Plan after the devastation of World War II, especially in respect to their scientific and industrial capacity which was conditioned by the interests of the victors of the war. There was no such Marshall Plan for India in spite of its seminal role in support of the Allied victory in World War II in general and in rolling back the Japanese invasion of India in 1944 by the XIV Army which had more than two-thirds of Indian troops. Many people have over the years tended to compare the progress made by these countries during the second half of the 20th century. But it needs to be remembered that they had a pretty high level of scientific and technological capacity that helped to fight the Allies (who also had the resources of the colonial world to rely on) for a full five years. And they also had the benefit of the Marshall Plan to rebuild their industrial and economic capacity though no doubt channelled in a direction that served the US interests in strategic terms, tying them into a military economic and political alliance, the benefits of which were not available to the developing countries that sought American military alliance like Pakistan did. Hence, comparisons with today's industrialised countries cannot provide us the model that India could have adopted. On the other hand, Pakistan, where agricultural growth had been high and as was the jute industry in East Pakistan, sought and obtained military aid and economic assistance from the US and its allies soon after its creation. But Pakistan's economy and industrial capacity have been on a downward spiral for the past three decades and the country is perpetually on an economic life support system from the Western powers that are not asking it to redirect its policies to achieve self-reliance.

Chinese Experience Before Mao Zedong

On the face of it, China could be seen to have the basic conditions similar to those of India after World War II. It has made enormous progress, far more than India, during the past three decades. But three facts must be borne in mind: China was well ahead of India even in 1750 in their share of global manufacturing output; China was not colonised the way India was (it still complains of "humiliation" by the imperial powers, not colonial rule); and it had unprecedented access at an enormous scale to civil and military technology from the former Soviet Union (during the early years till 1962, and again after 1992) and the Western powers (till at least the Tiananmen incident in 1989), while India was under the burden of extensive denial regime-based sanctions.

On the other hand, both are ancient civilisations which produced extraordinary technological achievements in many fields. We also must accept that historically, the literati elites in both civilisations did not develop the mental ethos associated with scientific investigations, such as scepticism, innovation, and inquiry into the unknown, processes associated with scientific and technological development. But unlike India, which was under direct rule and control by colonial Britain during the crucial two centuries when the scientific-industrial revolution expanded, which denied India a scientific and industrial revolution, China had been adversely affected only in terms of some economic and trade policies by foreign powers. It had the requisite autonomy to initiate a technological-industrial revolution but its elites were not interested in developing science and technology during the crucial 18th and 19th centuries. The net result was similar to that of India's deindustrialisation in the decline of its share in global manufacturing output. Richard Baum has pointed out that "China's major achievements were in the areas of observation rather than conceptualisation, concrete thinking rather than theoretical conceptualisation, deduction rather than induction, arranging ideas in patterns rather than developing theories to explain patterns."[14]

It was in the early 20th century that the "humiliation" by the Western powers, the Japanese war against China [and the KMT's (Kuomingtang's) need for American assistance], and disillusionment with Confucianism led to idealisation of Western scientific achievements, and science and technology began to be seen as a solution to all problems in an increasingly fractured society and policy, that finally led to the civil war and the replacement of the KMT with the Communist Party as the dominant ruler. Mao's own formula for human superiority over science and technology led to frequent tussles between pro-

technology development and those who opposed it. Mao's efforts
to bridge the gap through his experiments like the Cultural
Revolution, even after having manufactured the nuclear bomb,
only created serious difficulties in modernisation and growth
of science and technology. However, the great difference with
India was the enormously large Chinese population that had
started to mingle with American society (especially in Western
America) and life in the United States (something that began
in India's case actually in any significant numbers only during
the past two decades) that created the knowledge of a world
under the scientific-technological dispensation.

But the establishment of the People's Republic of China
(PRC) emulated the Stalinist model in almost all fields
of science and technology under state control. The more
independent minded scientists and technologists moved to
America; and some of them returned, initially when the PRC
took over the country, and later especially in the post-Mao-
Deng era when the Four Modernisations strategy brought
in fundamental reforms in the scientific and manufacturing
sectors. Essentially, these reforms created new conditions
for change in the long held organisational and functional
practices where research activities were isolated from the
production activities. The research activities, concentrated
under the Chinese Academy of Sciences (CAS), and the
industrial ministries were guided by a central plan (based
on the Soviet model). The research system was vertically
organised, with little horizontal interchange with the
manufacturing industry, and serious handicaps existed in
getting innovations from research laboratories to the factory
floors. The fact that all this was centrally controlled by political
leaders of various shades, with little understanding of science
and technology, did not help matters. For half a century,

India has built up a commendable capacity for research and manufacture; but their vertical and horizontal disjunction is no less than what existed in China in the Mao period when it could build hundreds of F-7s (the original early model of the Soviet MiG-21) since 1954, but could not really improve them till the Russians came back to help after 1992. What India needs is the type of reforms that Deng introduced and the time for such reforms came nearly a decade ago while we waited with bated breath! (More of it later.)

India's Industrial Structure

In his seminal work, Baldev Nayar had concluded, "The industrial structure that the Government of India inherited in 1947 had two major features. First, even though it was substantial and undoubtedly important in the Indian economy, it had a minor place in the total economy of India. Second, while Indian industry had made considerable advance in simple consumer goods and some progress in the direction of consumer durables, *it was utterly deficient in capital goods*"[15] (emphasis added). This serious deficit in the industrial system, along with a poverty-stricken population, created a twin-problem: that of lack of resources and the absence of a local market of an otherwise large population. Going back to the period immediately after India gained independence, the government realised that in order to industrialise the country, it must rely on liberal import of technology across a broad spectrum though this would have to be licensed where necessary and/or feasible. At the same time, foreign investments would be necessary (within the framework of serving national interests) to provide for the long-term objective of creating self-reliant industrial capacity for which the highest priority was the establishment of heavy industry.

Soon after its establishment, the Government of India had adopted the Industrial Policy Resolution 1948 laying down the broad guidelines of the industrial policy it intended to follow. The central logic of the policies emanating from this resolution was that: [16]

> In the present state of the nation's economy, when the mass of the people are below subsistence level, the emphasis should be on the expansion of production, both agricultural and industrial; and in particular on the production of capital equipment of goods satisfying the basic needs of the people and of commodities the export of which will increase the earnings of foreign exchange.

Based on these and other considerations, the government also decided that *"the manufacture of arms and ammunition, the production and control of atomic energy, and ownership and management of railway transport should be the exclusive monopoly of the Central Government"*[17] (emphasis added). In addition, in any emergency, the government would have the power to take over any industry vital for national defence. The industries listed to be under the control of the state included "aircraft manufacture" and "shipbuilding." The Industrial Resolution also laid down other priorities and included a host of industries which would be under the central government "regulation and control."

A major and immediate goal flowing from the Great Bengal Famine and the loss of canal irrigated lands to Pakistan (the area which used to be referred to as the granary of India) was to develop agriculture so as to increase foodgrain output. The Planning Commission was established in 1950 (the year India became a republic) and it prepared the First Five-Year Plan for the period 1951-56.[18] In spite of the urgency of catering for creating industrial capacity, the Fist Plan gave much higher priority to agriculture in order to try and reduce the acute shortage of foodgrain in the country. Nearly 38.5 percent of the total planned expenditure was to be spent on agriculture and its related activities. In comparison, industry, received a mere 8.4 percent of the Plan outlay. This is understandable, since even planning, leave alone building, major industrial enterprises, would take time. But mega projects for irrigation (like the Damodar Valley Project, Hirakud Dam, Bhakra Dam and its canal system, etc.) and the power generation system were planned and began to be built. The US economic aid under PL 480, especially for supply of foodgrain, also began to meet the crucial and endemic deficiency of foodgrain.

The First Plan must necessarily be treated as an interim and tentative attempt to lay down the foundations of future planning which sought an annual average economic growth rate of 2.5 percent during the Plan period, the actual growth exceeding this modest goal. Compared to it, the Second Five-Year Plan 1956-61, set itself what must be termed as an overambitious goal to double the Plan outlay and achieve an average increase of national income at the rate of 5 percent per annum, placing emphasis on heavy industry. The plan document stated:[19]

> In the long-run, the rate of industrialisation and the growth of the national economy would depend upon the increasing production of coal, electricity, iron and steel, heavy machinery, heavy chemicals, and the heavy industries generally which would increase the capacity for capital formation.... The heavy industries must, therefore, be expanded with all speed.

Towards the end of the First Plan period, the government issued a revised Industrial Policy Resolution in 1956.[20] The government had formally accepted the "the socialist pattern of society" as the objective of social and economic policy in December 1954. Industrial policy, therefore, henceforth must be governed by these principles and directions like the other policies in accordance with the Constitution of India. The Industrial Policy Resolution 1956 laid down that, "In order to realise this objective, it is essential to accelerate the rate of economic growth and to speed up industrialisation and, *in particular, to develop heavy industries and machine making industries, to expand the public sector, and to build up a large and growing cooperative sector"* (emphasis added). The resolution also revised and, where needed, expanded the industries under three categories. Those listed under Schedule A would be exclusively under state control while those under Schedule B would consist of industries "which will be progressively state-owned and in which the state will, therefore, generally take the initiative in establishing new undertakings, but in which private enterprise will also be expected to supplement the effort of the state." Schedule C would apply to all other remaining industries which were left to the initiative and enterprise of the private sector. From our perspective in the context of the present study, Schedule A industries (under exclusive state control) included the following:

- Arms and ammunition and allied items of defence equipment.
- Atomic energy.
- Aircraft.
- Air transport.
- Railway transport.
- Shipbuilding.

Interestingly, aluminium (a key metal extensively used in defence, especially in aircraft) was placed in Schedule B perhaps because the most extensive use of aluminium at that time, even after major production factories were set up, was for utensils and not aircraft, clearly indicating the state of the impoverished nation and the aspirations of its people.

As noted earlier, the Second Five-Year Plan 1956-61, doubled the government outlay with about 77.5 percent being provided for industry, to be spent on heavy industry, with social services and agriculture getting a lower share than in the First Plan. Relevant to our study also is the term "self-reliance," especially in defence. In principle, self-reliance was a natural corollary (or the other side of the coin) of the principle and strategy of non-alignment and independent foreign policy. The term came into greater use by the end of the Second Plan and the Third Plan stated this as the objective at various points in the Plan using terminologies like "self-reliant and self-sustained growth," making the economy "self-reliant and self-generating," building up a "self-reliant economy."[21] The Planning Commission had stated even in respect of self-reliance, "Self-Reliance not only means freedom from dependence on foreign aid but also involves the establishment of an acceptable minimum standard of living for the masses and a continuing rise in this standard."[22]

Here we need to focus a little more on industrial requirements and self-reliance for defence needs. The Indian Air Force (IAF) had its first experience of the consequences of dependence on external sources for weapons and equipment during the 1947-48 War launched by Pakistan when spares for aircraft became difficult to access even from surplus stocks of World War II. At the same time, India had sought to purchase the Spitfire XVIII which was agreed to by Britain (especially since they would be paid out of blocked sterling funds); but there were no stocks in the UK. The only new Spitfires were still lying at Karachi, and

Pakistan, at war with India, promptly impounded them. Luckily, the personal efforts of Air Chief Marshal Sir Thomas Elmhirst, C-in-C and Chief of the Air Staff (CAS) of (then Royal) the Indian Air Force helped to get the aircraft to India. The second jolt came in the crisis of 1951 when the armed forces were mobilised for a war threatened by Pakistan. It was found that the British supplied Vampire aircraft, at that time the frontline fighter of the IAF, was actually deficient of crucial parts necessary for its guns to operate. This led to the search for a second source for its weapons and the French Ouragon (Toofani in the IAF) was selected for acquisition.[23]

In its broader context, Prime Minister Nehru spoke on the relationship between heavy industry and defence while addressing the Lok Sabha at some length in 1956 when he conceded that India was not adequately prepared for modern warfare and went on to state:[24]

> What is the question of defence? In what lies the strength of a people for defence? Well, one thinks immediately about defence forces — army, navy and air force. Perfectly right. They are the spear points of defence. They have to bear the brunt of any attack. How do they exist? What are they based on? The more technical armies and navies and air forces get, the more important becomes the industrial and technological base of the country.

It is quite likely that the recent experiences of the IAF were very much on his mind, and no doubt so were the rising threats of Chinese incursions in Aksai Chin, followed as they were by the US-Pakistan military alliance and transfer of sophisticated arms by the US to Pakistan. To the critics who wanted the Five-Year Plans put aside in order to concentrate on defence, Nehru answered sharply: *"But the Five-Year Plan is the defence plan of the country.* What else is it? Because defence does not consist in people going about marching up and down the road with guns and other weapons. Defence consists today in a country being industrially prepared for producing the goods and equipment for defence"[25] and regretted that they had not started thinking about this earlier. (Emphasis added.)

The Blackett Report

A number of scientists had been invited to India just before and after independence to seek their views and recommendations on how best could India develop defence science and industry. One of the more prominent such scientists was Dr. P.M.S. Blackett, who was invited to India by the Government of India a number of times in the late 1940s to give advice on how to build the requisite science and technology base related to defence needs in India. In September 1948, he was specifically asked to address the scientific problems of defence in relation to the needs of the Indian armed forces.[26] In the covering letter to his report to the Indian Defence Minister, he emphasised that he "felt it necessary to widen very appreciably the scope of my enquiries and analyses to include a discussion of the wider problems of defence of India" from the given charter "to advise on organisation of defence science in relation to the needs of the Indian armed forces." Hence, he wrote, "I have ventured to take upon myself the task of attempting to discuss in some detail the relationship between (a) defence science; (b) military strategy; and (c) political and domestic industrial policies of India."

In the covering letter, Blackett also referred to the 1946 report by Dr. H. Wansborough Jones on a proposed scientific organisation for the armed forces, indicating that he agreed with Dr. Jones' conclusions and assumptions to make "India as early as possible a self-supporting defence entity as may be at the earliest possible date...." Jones' report had indicated that although he had earlier assumed that India would remain inside the Commonwealth of Nations (probably with Dominion status and, hence, substantial military assistance would be available to it from outside sources), he had recognised that the policy had changed and India would seek to stand "unaided, and the aim of development of her fighting Services should be directed to this end." Based on a note for the Defence Committee dated October 6, 1947, he took as guidance the role of the Indian armed forces as approved by the *interim government* in 1946 to be as follows:

- To secure the land frontier of India against raids of border tribes, or attacks by a second class army approximately equivalent to the Afghan Army.
- Support of civil power (this function was later deleted).
- To provide a small expeditionary force which should be available to proceed oversees at a reasonably short notice to protect Indian interests in the vicinity of India.
- To organise such formations and establishments as can be provided out of available financial resources, to form a nucleus for the expansion of the Army into an Army capable of taking the field in a first class war.

Blackett's judgement (and the government's acceptance of it) must be immediately questioned in regard to adopting the first assumption at sub-para (a) above. This may have been Dr. Jones' assumption in 1946, (perhaps when the partition of the country was still not seen as finite and final), and even that of the note for the Defence Committee of the Cabinet dated October 6, 1947, before the Pakistani invasion of J&K and the state's formal and legal accession to India, making New Delhi responsible for the defence of J&K as its national territory.

But after Pakistan attacked J&K on October 22, 1947 (and J&K's formal accession to India on October 26, 1947), the environment had changed dramatically, especially since India was complaining even to the UN that Pakistani aggression was largely based on the use of its army and specific units had been identified. This indicates Blackett's naivete in assuming almost one year after Pakistan attacked India in the J&K sector (and when even Pakistan had admitted to the UN Commission for India and Pakistan that its army was fighting inside J&K) that Indian defence would require a capability only against tribal raids or *"attacks by a second class army approximately equivalent to the Afghan Army."* After all, the Pakistan Army had been carved out of the British Indian Army at the time of the creation of Pakistan in August 1947, and it was far bigger and superior than the then Afghan Army, and had an air force with three squadrons of fighter aircraft and half a squadron of transports, besides an element of the navy. Blackett, in his report rendered in September 1948, appears to have consciously avoided the issue of a threat from Pakistan whose military was fighting the Indian armed forces for eleven months by that time. A second serious problem was that the Blackett Report was accepted by the Government of India. And, hence, a basic flaw in the thinking about India's needs of defence and defence equipment was introduced at the very inception itself. But worse follows when Blackett asserts that a war "against an opponent of comparable strength could hardly be other than mainly a land war with the air arm playing an important but subsidiary role, perhaps combined with coastwise combined operations."

Blackett goes on to cite Dr. Jones' report at para 8 (b) which stated, "Treating the defence problem, as a whole, the maintenance of the armed forces must be based on civil economy and it would be futile to develop well-trained and adequately equipped armed forces without sufficient civil and industrial forces to maintain them." However, this is where the real problem existed, as explained in the last chapter. On the eve of independence, India had virtually no defence industry (beyond the handful factories making rifles and ammunition) and a very limited civil industrial base beyond textile mills and the odd steel manufacturing plants of the Tatas. Many scholars have included tea, etc. when assessing the industrial capacity; but the tea "industry" would better fit into the agro-industry category with little spin-off for any defence industry beyond the foreign exchange earnings. Overall, Indian industrial production in India in 1945 was in the order of 2 percent of the British production in per capita terms. Not surprisingly, all the weapons and equipment of the Indian armed force in 1947 were of British origin with a smaller proportion from the United States.

Broadly speaking, Blackett divided all weapons into two categories: *competitive* weapons and *non-competitive* (simpler and basic) arms which in modern parlance would translate to high-technology high-performance/heavy weapons and low-technology basic weapons. In view of India's very weak economy and a near absence of military industry, Blackett's formula for India's arms acquisition strategy was that it should focus on weapons which would normally fall under the category of *non-competitive arms preferably to be acquired from British war surplus stocks* which might be available at low prices. Hence, military strategy would also have to be tailored accordingly. The so-called competitive weapons, he argued, should be acquired in small numbers and only when unavoidable. It was only in the case of Indian Navy that Blackett, not surprisingly, was willing to make generous deviations from this principle. The requirement of a rapid self-reliant military technical capabilities, according to Blackett, was to be achieved in three parts:[27]

- The demand for the manufacture in India at the earliest date of the simple weapons.
- The working out of a general defence strategy and also of detailed military tactics to reduce for the time being the need for complicated weapons which India cannot soon manufacture, in favour of the simpler ones she can.
- The preparation of long period plans for the manufacture of high performance and complicated weapons in India as soon as the technological level of India, and the degree of industrialisation has risen sufficiently to make it possible.

In essence, Blackett spelt out a plan that took into account India's extremely low level of industrialisation and weak economy, hence, recommending that defence expenditure be kept at the lowest level possible (possibly below the then figure of around 2 percent of the national income) not only for its own sake, but as a route to higher technology weapons for defence at a later date. Air forces, by their very nature rely upon high technology weapons and equipment. Hence, this approach was bound to affect the Indian Air Force more than the other two Services. Blackett complained more than once that his discussions with the chiefs (Two British and one Indian in 1948) of the three military Services did not result in a commonly agreed perception.

The chiefs, he wrote later, presented plans for very large quantities of modern weapons and equipment, the acquisition of which for one year would absorb the whole year's defence budget. But, curiously, Blackett does not even once mention the ongoing war launched by the Pakistan military in J&K. Blackett greatly emphasised the building up of the Indian Navy and an aircraft carrier for it. As regards the IAF, he ruled out any large heavy bomber which the Emergency Committee

of the Cabinet (ECC) of the Indian Cabinet authorised in
1963 after the Sino-Indian War. In fact, he was against India
acquiring even jet fighters, concluding that they were too fast
to provide close support to the Army, thus, also indicating
that he was not well versed with the theory and practice of
air power. As Chris Smith writes, "All or most of the advice he
(Blackett) gave cut against the grain of military professional
interests ....." and he should have added, professional
judgement based on extensive experience of the recently
concluded World War.[28]

Smith cites the Blackett papers to record that Blackett
in effect had argued against the advice of the three Service
Commanders-in-Chief (all British at that time) — which he
termed as "wild" with respect to their recommendations to
build India's defence capabilities. He cites that:[29]

> I usually managed to speak to the Joint Chiefs of Staff meeting. But
> I am not of any official status in defence matters. I found it very
> interesting and I think it was useful getting to know a country which
> has got independence. You got some advice from the old British
> advisers, which may or may not suit the occasion. Then there was
> very dangerous advice, it was hard to get objective advice and I had
> a lot to do ...... I think I saved India a lot of money by discouraging
> her from some of the wilder ideas that the Chiefs of Staff had when
> I went there ......

Blackett's coverage of the role and organisation of
defence science in Indian defence is more valuable than
his expedition into threat identification, force structure
and military strategy. His most valuable and insightful
contribution was in respect of defence science and its
organisation. It will be useful to cite at some length on this
subject from the report:[30]

To avoid any misconception, as to the role of the scientific staff of the Scientific Adviser, it is recommended that the research activities of the Development Establishment should remain at present an integral part of the establishments and so under the control of D.T.D. The *Scientific Adviser to the Defence Ministry should clearly have the right to be consulted on the research programmes and on appointment of scientific staff, etc., but should not, at present, at any rate, have any executive responsibility in relation to the research activities of the establishment.* In a few years time, when the Scientific Adviser has a staff adequately trained in the different branches of defence science, the position could be reviewed. If a new establishment, such as an aeronautical establishment, is formed, this will clearly be mainly staffed by civilians from the outset. How best such an establishment should fit into the organisational scheme will want careful consideration.

Thus, at present, *Indian Defence Science will follow more the organisational pattern of the British Admiralty than the Army or Air Force. In the foremost, the research and development establishments are under Service control and usually have a Service officer as Director, and with the Director of Scientific Research fulfilling a mainly advisory role.* In the latter, the establishments have civilian heads and are under the direct control of the Chief Scientist at the Ministry of Supply. The latter system has many advantages but demands more trained civilian defence scientists than India at present possesses (emphasis added).

This was a crucial recommendation which would have a far-reaching impact on not only defence science but also on self-reliance in weapon systems. The Indian Navy, no doubt taking a leaf from the practice in the Royal Navy, set up the Directorate of Warship Design and associated institutions like Weapons and Electronic System Engineering Establishment (WESEE) and Controller of Warship Construction, within and integral to the Naval Headquarters. This, over the decades, has made the Navy the prime stakeholder in warship design, development and production besides subsequent upgrades, and so on, with obvious remarkably positive results as may be seen in the Delhi class destroyers, and so on. Regrettably, in spite of their extensive workshops, many of which had constituted the foundations of expansion for defence production during World War II to produce ordnance and related stores, and the IAF's BRDs (Base Repair Depots) with trained technical manpower, the Indian Army and the Indian Air Force remained detached from design and development over the past six decades, except at the very inception of a programme when the General Staff Qualitative Requirements (GSQR)/Air Staff Requirements (ASR) are defined and toward the end when the new weapon system is offered for trials. Merely attaching some military officers to sort out some specific issues only amounts to spasmodic ad-hoc interest when things are going wrong. What we are talking about is the systemic approach to design and development and the role of military professionals and defence scientists in this process. To this, has to be added the role of the manufacturer; but we will come to that later.

Blackett made detailed recommendations on the type of weapon systems that India should acquire and build for each of the three Services. He rejected outright any long range bombers but failed to mention the inevitable linkage between the long range heavy bomber and transport aircraft in the evolution of the aircraft industry the world over. In fact, *he did not make any recommendation regarding transport aircraft for a geographically vast country like India* except to note tentatively: "Consideration might perhaps later be given to the production under licence of such a general purpose transport aircraft as the Dakota."[31] There is little evidence beyond this oblique remark in the available literature about civil/military transport aircraft till Krishna Menon, as the Defence Minister, at the urging of Air Vice Marshal Harjinder Singh, set up the Aircraft Manufacturing Depot (AMD) at Kanpur as an IAF organisation, with technical personnel drawn from the Air Force in 1960 to manufacture the HS-748 Avro under licence.

But it is surprising that Blackett should have ignored transport aircraft for all practical purposes in his report of September 1948 when everyone knew that Kashmir had been saved by mobilising 100-odd sorties in one day, transporting troops from Delhi to Srinagar on October 27, 1947, after the state formally acceded to India. There were already nearly 21 civil airlines flying over 200 transport aircraft in the country. Much earlier, India had been the first country to initiate carriage of mail by air in February 1910, a mere year after the first aircraft came to India. As early as 1917, the question of introducing air transport in India was under discussion of the Indian government as a consequence of the great progress made in development of aircraft during World War I. In September 1919, the Government of India accepted the proposal to allow a monopoly of a single company to carry mail throughout the country.

In the pre-war years, mail rather than passengers dominated the airline service in India. But immediately after the end of World War II, there was a boom in air transport enterprise. War-surplus Dakotas were available at as low a price as Rs. 20,000 each and another Rs. one lakh was required to convert each one to civil airline standards which HAL, now relieved of the overhaul role for the USAAF, was able to carry out efficiently. By early 1947, 21 companies with an authorised capital of Rs. 42 crore were registered.[32] By the end of June 1951, the number of aircraft (not counting those in the IAF) registered in India was 738 and over 200 aircraft held current certificate of airworthiness.[33] We need to recall here that India at that stage had a full-fledged aircraft factory at HAL, Bangalore. Even a brief look at the civil transport aircraft needs of that period indicates the potential for a viable aircraft manufacturing industry in India. For example, during the pre-war years, with a global economic depression going on, India imported a total of 171 transport aircraft during the five years between 1934-38 at a total cost of Rs. 42.99 lakh. This would theoretically amount to an annual average production/acquisition of 34 aircraft at a cost of Rs. 8.6 lakh — a task that a fledgling aircraft factory like HAL could have easily undertaken.

The number of transport aircraft for military and civil uses only kept increasing after that. But the logic of manufacturing transport aircraft escaped the attention of policy-makers and their advisers. The aircraft industry worldwide found it useful and even perhaps necessary toward the mid-20th century that transport aircraft and bombers had a lot in common and, hence, one or the other became a by-product, depending upon actual circumstances. The tragedy, among many others, for the Indian aircraft industry was that the public sector undertaking run by civil bureaucrats in the Ministry of Defence remained oblivious to the issues and role of transport aircraft in building a national aircraft industry. Hence, through the following six decades, HAL, even after the IAF's Aircraft Manufacturing Depot (AMD) at Kanpur was taken over by it in 1964, did not build on the experience of the HS-748 Avro licensed produced transport aircraft. In fact, its Kanpur division regressed to smaller light transport aircraft manufacture under licence (like the Dornier 228) after the Avro production ended, while at its main establishment at Bangalore, hangars, machinery and manpower remained underutilised for decades.

Going back to the economic and civil aviation picture of the pre-war years that led to Walchand Hirachand setting up the aircraft industry in Bangalore in 1939 (the details are given in a later chapter), before World War II, the Government of India acquired shares in HAL and "promised to purchase, in the first instance, fifty aircraft per year."[34] Unfortunately, there is little evidence that we could find as to why HAL did not undertake manufacture of transport aircraft (even under licence) after the war when the existing stocks could have provided the cushion for the new airline industry.

On the other hand, the impact of two centuries of deindustrialisation is perhaps best appreciated in comparing the defence production for World War II between the United States and India. But India was severely handicapped not only by the absence of an aircraft industry (though one factory was set up in 1940), but also of raw materials like high quality steel, aluminium, etc and the near absence of supporting subsidiary industries. HAL, set up as a private joint venture supported by the Maharaja of Mysore, with the Government of India as a shareholder, overhauled over 3,000 engines and 1,271 aircraft (mostly American heavy bombers, transport aircraft and light bombers) during World War II. But it did not manufacture any aircraft. As noted earlier, the Tatas' proposal to manufacture the Mosquito fighter-bomber as a private venture was stymied by the British government in New Delhi after approval had been accorded.

The contrast, on the other hand, may be seen in the output of the United States, which held a negligible share of global manufacturing output two centuries earlier. Between 1941-45, the US alone designed and produced approximately 300,645 aircraft during the war years, besides the repair and overhaul of a large number of these aircraft! In addition, besides its massive warship construction, the United States produced 2.228 million trucks, 88,410 tanks, and 489,838 pieces of artillery during the war.[35]

Notes

1. Prime Minister Jawaharlal Nehru, Address at the Annual Session in Federation of Indian Chambers of Commerce and Industry (FICCI), 1963, *Proceedings of the Twenty-sixth Annual Session Held in New Delhi on March 16, 17, and 18, 1963* (New Delhi: Federation House, 1963), p. 12.

2. Subimal Dutt, *With Nehru in the Foreign Office* (Calcutta, 1977), p.22.

3. Jawaharlal Nehru, *India's Foreign Policy: Selected Speeches, September 1946-April 1961* (New Delhi, 1961), p. 574.

4. Ibid., pp. 2-3.

5. Ibid., p. 2. See also Nehru's speech on December 13, 1946, in *Jawaharlal Nehru's Speeches*, Vol. I, Ministry of Information and Broadcasting (Delhi: The Publications Division), pp. 5-16.

6. Ibid., p. 241.

7. *New China Agency*, November 21, 1949.

8. For example, see Nehru's statement in 1959, "Ever since the Chinese Revolution, we naturally had to think of what China was likely to be. ..... We realised — we knew that amount of history — that a strong China is normally an expansionist China. Throughout history, that has been the case. And we felt that the great push towards industrialisation of that country, plus the amazing pace of its population increase, would together create a most dangerous situation. Taken also with the fact of China's somewhat inherent tendency to be expansive when it is strong, we realised the danger to India.... As the years have gone by, this fact has become more and more apparent and obvious. If any person imagines that we have followed our China policy without realising the consequences, he is mistaken." (Jawaharlal Nehru, *India's Foreign Policy*, p.369).

9. Baldev Raj Nayar, *India's Quest for Technological Independence: Policy Foundations and Policy Change*, Vol. 1 (New Delhi: Lancer International, 1983), p. 134.

10. Ajay Singh, "Quest for Self-Reliance," in Jasjit Singh, *India's Defence Spending* (New Delhi: Knowledge World, 2001, 2nd edition).

11. Dr V. Siddhartha, *The Triple-Trap, Dual-Use and the Single Reform*, Unpublished presentation at a seminar on Defence Research & Development organised by Defence Accounts Department, CGDA, Delhi, June 10, 2006.

12. Amiya Kumar Bagchi, *Private Investment in India 1900-1939* (Cambridge, Cambridge University Press, 1972), pp. 25, 420-421.

13. *Report of the Indian Industrial Commission 1916-18*, Vol. I, reprinted edition (Calcutta, 1934), p. 164.

14. Richard Baum, "Science and Culture in Contemporary China," *Asian Survey*, December 1982, p. 1170.

15. Nayar, n.9, pp. 146-47.

16. India, *Industrial Policy Resolution 1948*, No. 1(3)-44(13)/48, New Delhi, April 6, 1948, para 2.

17. Ibid., para 4.

18. India, Planning Commission, *The First Five-Year Plan* (New Delhi, 1953).

19. P.C. Mahalanobis, "Draft Recommendations for the Formulation of the Second Five-Year Plan 1956-61," in India, Planning Commission, *Papers Relating to the Formulation of the Second Five-Year Plan, 1955* (Delhi: Manager of Publications, 1962), p. 31

20. See India, *Industrial Policy Resolution 1956*, No. 91/SF/48, New Delhi, April 30, 1956.

21. The two terms "self-reliance" and "self-sufficiency" have been rhetorically used interchangingly, but the term "self-sufficiency " was used in the Planning Commission documents only in the context of foodgrains.

22. India, Planning Commission, *Fourth Five-Year Plan: A Draft Outline* (New Delhi, 1960), p. 24.

23. Air Marshal M.S. Chaturvedi, *History of the Indian Air Force* (New Delhi: Vikas Publishing House, 1978), pp. 103-104. A great deal of credit for this decision also goes to Air Marshal C.E. Gibbs, Commander-in-Chief, Indian Air Force, who, according to Chaturvedi, was in favour of buying the British Gloster Meteor fighter, but in spite of his own bias in favour of the Meteor, conceded to the recommendations of the Plans Branch for the French fighter. See Chaturvedi, Ibid., p. 110.

24. Jawaharlal Nehru, Speech during debate on Demands of the Ministry of Defence, Lok Sabha, March 21, 1956, in *Jawaharlal Nehru's Speeches: Vol Three: March 1953-August 1957*, Ministry of Information and Broadcasting (Delhi: The Publications Division, 1958), pp. 39-40.

25. Ibid., pp. 41-42.

26. P.M.S. Blackett, A Report to the Hon'ble The Defence Minister on *Scientific Problems of Defence in Relation to the Needs of the Indian Armed Forces* (New Delhi: September 10, 1948).

27. Ibid., p. 6.

28. Chris Smith, *India's Ad Hoc Arsenal: Direction or Drift in Defence Policy?* (New York: Oxford University Press – SIPRI, 1994), p. 53.

29. Transcript of radio interview with P.M.S. Blackett, Blacket Papers G-12 (Royal Society Archives, London), pp. 2-3 cited in Smith, Ibid., p. 53.

30. Blackett, n.26, p. 6.

31. Ibid., p. 15.

32. M.R. Dhekney, *Air Transport in India (Growth and Problems)* (Bombay: Vora & Co. Publishers Ltd, 1953), p. 86.
33. Ibid., p. 91.
34. Ibid., p. 233.
35. Michael G. Carew, *Becoming the Arsenal: The American Industrial Mobilization for World War II, 1938-1942* (Lanham: University Press of America Inc., 2010), p. 178.

4

The Nehru Era
On the Road to Self-Reliance

> Research, design and development, manufacture and inspection are all integrated activities. *They must, therefore, be organisationally unified to obtain optimum results.*
>
> — Major General B.D. Kapur, former CCR&D[1]

After independence, and the adoption of a policy of non-alignment, it was also obvious that the foreign policy would need to be reinforced by a policy of self-reliance in defence. There were few doubts that India needed to stand on her own in fulfilling defence requirements. Prime Minister Jawaharlal Nehru believed that no country was truly independent, unless it was independent in matters of armament. It is curious that the language used while referring to defence needs in the early years after independence focussed on self-reliance, but this changed to self-sufficiency by the late 1960s and once again reverted to self-reliance in recent years. There is an essential difference in the two terms. Self-sufficiency in defence requires all stages in defence production (starting from design to manufacture, including raw materials) to be carried out within the country. To be self-sufficient, a country must not only have the material resources required for defence production, but also the technical expertise to undertake design and development without external assistance. Few countries have been self-sufficient in military weapons and systems design, development and manufacture except the Soviet Union and the United States. The former had to invest enormous human and technological resources (at the cost of a better quality of life for its people), while the latter progressively sought the collaboration of its allies often through a system of offsets and enhancing the economies of scale in production.

China was forced to adopt a policy for autonomous development of weapons and technology after the split with the Soviet Union in the late 1950s. But it could not really move along that direction in spite of substantive resources devoted to the endeavour. To compensate for the quality deficit of its weaponry due to obsolescence of technology of the late 1940s, it expanded its production capabilities trying to offset technological deficiency with sheer quantity. Finally, when it entered the phase of reforms to facilitate modernisation of the economy and industry, it enjoyed some advantages through technological cooperation with the US and the European Union (EU) countries; but this soon dried out when it came up against sanctions and technology-denial regimes after the 1989 Tiananmen Square incidents. But the collapse of the Soviet Union opened up an unanticipated opportunity to upgrade its technologies in key areas of military requirements and, hence, could rapidly modernise its design and development capabilities with Russian assistance. India probably was better placed than China, and the Prime Minister and the Defence Minister were supported, but the opportunity was lost in the corridors of South Block and the unwillingness of the Defence Public Sector Undertakings (DPSUs). The Defence Research and Development Organisation (DRDO) was interested as long as Dr Arunachalam headed it, but with his departure, forward thinking suffered a setback.

As is clear from the earlier chapters, India after independence was in no position to be "self-sufficient" in defence equipment, and, hence, the shift to a quest for self-reliance was a natural outcome from the very beginning. Self-reliance differs from self-sufficiency in that it does not preclude accessing external sources for technology and systems, or external help at any stage of the production cycle. Although it may seem paradoxical, a country can be self-reliant at a fairly high level, approaching self-sufficiency in specific areas by cooperating with other countries, for technology transfer even if it is only for production purposes, and creating interdependencies that serve as a form of insurance. The litmus test of self-reliance is the degree of dependency on external sources which actually results in vulnerability to changes of policy by the other country. Being in a position where self-reliance had to be achieved from a deindustrialised stage, India opted for an incremental path along a *balanced model of self-reliance* in defence requirements. For self-reliance to be achieved, it was necessary to continue to improve the economy and meet urgent requirements through imports while starting work on indigenous capabilities.

The self-reliance model adopted in practice can best be described as one that fundamentally relied on diversification in the sources of weapons and military technology, while working on establishing and expanding the indigenous base for design, development, and manufacture of weapons and equipment. But to achieve even that at an ever expanding scale and quality, less industrialised countries like India (or China) have to go through a series of sequential steps along an almost linear path, starting with repair and overhaul at the bottom to serve as the foundation.[2] While many optimists would seek to leapfrog technological advancement, the reality is that without a wide base of national industrial capacity and the specific capabilities, as outlined in Fig 4.1, the success would be ephemeral, with a high potential for counter-productive results.

Fig 4.1: Steps Toward Indigenous Self-Reliance in Defence Industry

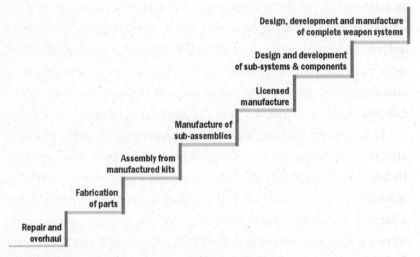

Source: Adapted from Ajay Singh, "Quest for Self-Reliance" in Jasjit Singh, *India's Defence Spending* (New Delhi: Knowledge World, 2000) 2nd edition, p. 128.

In terms of repair and overhaul, the expansion of World War II to the Pacific theatre and up to India's borders had not only necessitated the setting up of such facilities in India, but also given the process a certain impetus. The ordnance factories and railway workshops had been performing such functions at the lowest level of technological capabilities. Their tasks and roles were expanded. But in some cases, the war effort led to a reversal in the process of growth of indigenous defence industrial capabilities, especially with respect to indigenous design, development and manufacture which had been set up in 1940. For example, as covered in the previous chapter, the privately owned Hindustan Aircraft was taken over by the

British Indian government and allocated the task of repair and overhaul of US Army Air Force (USAAF) aircraft operating in the Southeast Asia Command of the Allies. By the time the war ended, the factory had overhauled a large number of aircraft and engines. But the earlier efforts and capabilities to start design and development had atrophied; and the post-war demobilisation and rapid drop in overhaul tasks had led to the factory shrinking down by June 1946 to as little as 3,740 employees (including 1,700 engineers, technicians and unskilled labour, the remaining being administrative and executive staff).

During the post-war years, HAL began to undertake overhaul and refurbishing of war surplus Dakotas and overhaul of Royal Indian Air Force aircraft like the Tempest II and the training aircraft like the Tiger Moth, etc. As noted in the previous chapter, a large number of transport aircraft had been abandoned or were available at throwaway prices. Hence, refurbishing of the Dakota transport aircraft for airline use was in great demand and, consequently, a large number of airlines mushroomed, enlarging the demand on HAL. In addition, HAL also began to undertake repair and overhaul, what in today's terminology would be called MRO (Maintenance, Repair and Overhaul) of aircraft of foreign airlines, especially Air France, Philippines Airlines and others that "got a better job and cheaper than from anywhere else," while HAL's engine division turned out overhauled engines, including the Pratt and Whitney 1830 and 1340, Bristol Centaurus, de Havilland Gypsy and others for various types of aircraft.[3] These developments gradually began to increase the financial turnover from a modest Rs. 57 lakh in 1946-47 to Rs. 130 lakh in 1947-48. Pakistan's invasion of Kashmir raised the requirement of civil transport aircraft and overhaul of the truncated Air Force (from 10 squadrons to six and a half squadrons) operating in support of the Army.[4] HAL's turnover for the following year (1948-49) rose to Rs. 180 lakh.

As the Pakistani invasion across the International Border began in the last week of October 1947, the Defence Minister proposed to the newly constituted Defence Committee of the Cabinet that the Indian Air Force should undertake bombing of a 10-km swath inside the western borders of the state of J&K to create a *cordon sanitaire* to deter and reduce the infiltration taking place from Pakistan. However, the C-in-C and Chief of the Air Staff, Air Chief Marshal Sir Thomas Elmhirst expressed the inability of the Air Force to achieve this effectively since there were no suitable aircraft in sufficient numbers. Elmhirst advocated the acquisition of old RAF war surplus Lancaster bombers after they had been overhauled in England. However, the legendary *Hawai Sipahi* Air Vice Marshal (then Wing Commander Technical at Air HQ) Harjinder Singh strongly opposed it on the grounds that its liquid-cooled Merlin engine would be totally unsuitable in the Indian climate.

Finding that Air HQ was proceeding with the proposed acquisition in spite of his adverse judgement, Harjinder resigned. When he was called to his office by Elmhirst, he insisted that there were over 50 Liberators in Kanpur which had been put out of action and could be restored to flying status. This triggered off the saga of reconstruction of the war surplus USAAF B-24 Liberator bombers dumped in one corner of Kanpur airfield which had already acquired the name "bomber graveyard." In fact, the British and American forces had ordered that all aircraft being left behind in India must be disabled or even destroyed. Harjinder told the chief's office that these 50 Liberators could be rebuilt and overhauled in India. Consequently, he was posted as Station Commander Kanpur and with the cooperation of HAL, a total of 40 Liberators was duly overhauled and declared fit for active flying.[5] The Liberators formed a squadron (No. 6 Squadron, RIAF) by November 1948 and served in the maritime reconnaissance role till the last aircraft was retired in 1967. HAL also took on the reconstruction and refurbishing of 150 Tiger Moths for the Air Force and flying clubs.

One of India's major challenges immediately after independence was to restore the size of weapons and the strength of its military forces;[6] and the Pakistani invasion of Kashmir lent greater urgency to the challenges. India had responded to the invasion by airlifting troops to Srinagar on October 27, 1947. On November 11, it sent a mission to London seeking over 100 aircraft [52 Tempest II, 60 Spitfire XVIII trainers, an unspecified number of jet aircraft, one twin-engine photo reconnaissance aircraft, an unspecified number of twin-engine bombers, 12 Dove communications aircraft) and seven naval vessels (including three destroyers)].[7] Nine days later, Pakistan approached the British manufacturer Hawkers asking for technical assistance and aircraft. Incidentally, as early as early mid-November, Pakistan tried to circumvent the Joint Defence Council's partition plan for the armed forces by making a direct request to the Commonwealth Relations Office in London (headed by Philip Noel-Baker known for his steering Western policies on Kashmir's legal accession to India to pursue support for Pakistan's aggression!) for 36,000 British rifles lying in Madras: and apparently succeeded in the process. India's search for small arms and ammunition after independence reemphasised the fragility of its defence industry in the middle of a war launched against it barely weeks after independence, two centuries after the Industrial Revolution had been in progress across the Western world.

Higher Defence Management

At this stage, it may be useful to briefly review the higher defence organisation as it was set up in September 1947 after independence. In substance, it was similar to the one existing in the other major parliamentary democracy, Great Britain, and the details were drawn from its vast experience of nearly two centuries with the Chiefs of Staff system. In principle, the higher defence organisation was established on the principle of corporate management (like the Cabinet itself and its various committees). The system as established was to function at three levels: (i) political authority at the apex level; (ii) political authority at the level of the Defence Minister acting through committees; and (iii) military professional level. The organisation can be briefly outlined as follows:

Committees Headed by Political Leaders

- **Defence Committee of the Cabinet** to deal on behalf of the Cabinet with all important questions relating to defence, both short-term as well as long-term. The Commanders-in-Chief of the three independent Services (the title of Chiefs of Staff was a subsidiary one) and the Defence Secretary were to be in attendance.
- **Defence Minister's Committee** which would give decisions on all important matters which jointly concern any two or all three Services but which do not require to be referred to the Defence Committee of the Cabinet.
- Three committees designated as *Defence Minister's (Army/Navy/Air Force) Committees* to consider major policy issues affecting that particular Service.

Committees Directly Under the Defence Minister

- **Chiefs of Staff Committee** originally set up to service the

Defence Committee of the Cabinet later modified to be the primary military authority to advise the Defence Minister and normally through him, the Defence Committee of the Cabinet.

Committees Directly Reporting to the Defence Minister's Committee

- **Principal Personnel Officers' Committee** reporting directly to the Defence Minister's Committee on matters dealing with service terms and conditions, discipline, recruitment, etc.
- **Principal Supply Officers' Committee** to advise the Defence Minister's Committee on inter-Service matters of policy regarding logistics.
- **Medical Services Committee** to advise the Defence Minister's Committee directly on matters of medical policy.
- **Defence Science Advisory Committee** to consider technical and scientific aspects of Service requirements, including close contact with research and development, production and basic science research.
- **New Weapons and New Equipment Production and Supply Committee** to coordinate the Services' requirement for production and supply of new weapons, munitions and equipment.

Committees Reporting to the Chiefs of Staff Committee (COSC)

- **Joint Planning Committee** to undertake planning for the COSC for the joint employment of the three Services.
- **Joint Intelligence Committee** headed by a Foreign Service officer to provide the COSC and Joint Planning Committee with all information relating to the situation, both inside as well as outside India, needed to enable them to discharge their functions.
- **Joint Administrative Planning Committee** to prepare joint

administrative plans to supplement the operational plans for future operations.

- **Service Communication Board** to advise the COSC on signals and communications matters.
- **Joint Training Committee** to consider new techniques of inter-Service support and cooperation, including modifications to tactical doctrine, employment of, and training in, equipment common to two or more Services.

One more committee titled **Defence Coordination Committee** in the Ministry of Defence was set up soon after. Interestingly, the political leader in the form of the Defence Minister was to be the ultimate decision-making authority for all matters below those required to be taken by the Cabinet (and he too was to function with a series of committees). For the purpose of our current study, the committees directly related to the aircraft industry were:

- **Defence Science Advisory Committee** to consider the technical and scientific aspects of Service requirements, including close contact with research and development, production and basic science research.
- **New Weapons and New Equipment Production and Supply Committee** to coordinate the Services' requirement for production and supply of new weapons, munitions and equipment.

The organisation below that level was still based on the British experience where aircraft were still under the Ministry of Supplies. But it was deeply linked to the military establishment. Major General B.D. Kapur, who was CCR&D (Chief Controller of Research and Development) in the 1950s, believed that a design has no value unless it has the approval of the producer.

It is in this context that he writes that the "British had military Controllers and Deputy Controllers in the erstwhile Ministry of Supply, which had stood the test of the Second World War in building up the defence R&D and supply effort of Britain. These officers reported direct to the Minister of Supply and were of the rank of Lieutenant General or Air Marshal, and were not the 'throw-pits' from the Army as it was in our case, but had been cleared for promotion to higher ranks!"[8]

But the British Admiralty had a different system where ship design and construction was controlled by the Admiralty officers. Fortunately, this system was inherited by the Indian Navy after independence and carries on till now, where the Naval HQ actually has a Directorate of Warship Design and also appointments of Controller of Warship Construction. The results have been clearly visible in that the Indian Navy, as the major stakeholder in future warships and weapons, has pressed for indigenous design, development and production over the decades for warships that would meet our operational and technological requirements. The Delhi class of destroyers is a case in point. The Indian Navy used the expertise of all sorts of organisations, including the two behemoths, the Council for Scientific and Industrial Research (CSIR) and DRDO. But it retained its stake in warship design and development while, at the other level, it retained management of the dockyards where ships were constructed and repaired.

The organisations under them had been inherited from the British War Office (Ministry of Defence) which was a civil-military integrated headquarters; but they soon began to be "reorganised" and provide the broad model of what was to happen to the nascent defence industry in India. For example, the Department of the Master General of Ordnance (MGO), which was the first to be fragmented after independence, used to be headed by the MGO as a Principal Staff Officer (PSO) in Army HQ was responsible for the procurement of weapons and equipment, their production, inspection, storage and maintenance, all interrelated and interacting activities.[9] Thus, the Directorate of Ordnance Services, the Electrical and Mechanical Engineering, Technical and Mechanical Engineering, Technical Development and the Director General of Ordnance Factories (DGOF) came under his charge. The reorganisation started with the DG Ordnance Factories being placed under the Ministry of Defence, followed by the Director of Technical Development and Inspectorate. Very soon, the DGOF, with a 60,000 strong work force, began to fail to meet the targets of production. The Baldev Singh (the first Defence Minister after independence) Committee Report had highlighted the deficiencies in the ordnance factories and their management.[10] According to Major General Kapur, the committee had suggested:

- To decentralise the management of 27-odd ordnance factories by grouping them product-wise and appointing Deputy Director Generals for each group; that is, armament and ammunition, clothing and equipment, and, process industries and metallurgy.
- To modernise machine tools, which were just about ticking over and to replace them with multi-purpose modern machines.
- To review the inventory and reduce the same to manageable stocks accumulated over the war years, and, to modernise the control system of the inventory.
- To stockpile strategic materials, particularly those that were imported.

But little concrete action was taken on this report.[11] The second most important aspect of the higher management of defence was the role and functions of the Scientific Adviser and the Defence Research and Development Organisation. At the time of independence, the Scientific Adviser was distinct and separate from any particular organisation and in principle and practice had no executive responsibilities although he was inevitably invited even to meetings on strategy and new weapons planning. Defence research establishments, even as they grew in numbers, were under a CCR&D (Chief Controller R&D) to head the defence science department which post in the mid-1950s was held by Major General B.D. Kapur. Professor D.S. Kothari, who continued to teach physics at the Delhi University, raised the Defence Science Organisation in 1948, and was the Honorary Scientific Adviser to the Defence Ministry till 1958 when he formally took over the post of Scientific Adviser to the Defence Minister.

Building Defence Science/Technology Institutions

History is consistent in the conclusion that Prime Minister Nehru's dedication and support to science and technology (including that for defence) was unmatched and was the one single factor that influenced the early growth of the country. How much this vision was understood, leave alone shared, by the civil and military bureaucracy down the line, barring a few notable exceptions, can be open to question. For example, the CSIR, headed by Sir Shanti Sarup Bhatnagar, established a chain of new national laboratories, like Britain had. The quantum of funding allocated, the adequacy of scientific manpower, and how much boost they could provide in the early years remained questionable and did not meet the expectations of many people. But viewed in the context of the deindustrialisation of India in the previous two centuries, the institutional basis of the laboratories was a critical foundation for the future though they would take time to prove their value. The important point is that to back up this national enterprise, five Indian Institutes of Technology (IITs) were also established for the education of highly professional scientific and technological manpower. Parallel to that, the Indian Institutes of Management (IIMs) provided professional education to exploit the emerging scientific and technological base in the early years of independence. Over time, many more institutions were established even though governmental control as defined in the Industrial Resolutions in 1948 and 1956 has tended to increase bureaucratic control, often by those with little knowledge of science and technological imperatives, rather than to provide assistance to industrialise the country.

The Comprehensive Self-Reliance Model

Looking back at history, what becomes obvious in terms of building a self-reliant aircraft industry is the adoption and implementation of a comprehensive interwoven, interrelated and interdependent model based on three strands as follows:

- Institute and progressively strengthen the design and development of aircraft to meet the future requirements of the Indian Air Force and the other two branches of the armed forces within HAL. Given the reality that this capability had been given up soon after HAL was established in 1940, the process would have to begin at the simplest level, that is, aircraft for primary flying training; obviously, this would be the most important strand that assumes the importance of the foundations of the future aircraft industry.

- Concurrently, begin a programme of licensed production of suitable aircraft to meet the Air Force's operational and training requirements. This would help to strengthen

HAL's production capabilities and technology besides providing experience and capacity for Maintenance, Repair and Overhaul (MRO) for the types of aircraft and systems being manufactured under licence.

- Direct purchase of modern, normally high-technology aircraft, required urgently and which would either take a long time to build under licence or were not available under terms that would allow licensed production. Normally, these would incorporate a smaller number of state-of-the-art technologies and operational capabilities that would fill some inevitable force structure gaps.

These strands did not have to be in any hierarchical order and would depend on both the capabilities for design and development, on one side, and production and product support, on the other. For a developing country with very little science, technology and industrial base, this was obviously the most optimised model to build an aircraft industry. It may be noted that most of the British technical advisers like Dr. P.M.S. Blackett, had advocated acquisition of "non-competitive" types of weapons which could be acquired (mainly from Britain) from the existing war surplus stocks, and the design and production of simple aircraft like basic trainers.

INDIGENOUS DESIGN AND DEVELOPMENT

It is in this context that we observe the post-independence aircraft industry, starting with reconstruction and overhaul of aircraft like the B-24 Liberators (in support of the IAF), overhaul and reconstruction of nearly 150 Tiger Moths and war-time residual Harvard aircraft (which allowed elementary flying training to begin immediately after independence). Concurrently, HAL began its first licensed production of aircraft with the manufacture of the Percival P.40 Prentice T.3 aircraft for flying training. The IAF needed flying training assets badly since it was to not only maintain the truncated size of 6-odd squadrons, and have sufficient pilots trained for the war in Kashmir, but also to rebuild the force back to at least the pre-independence strength of 10 squadrons. At the same time, a large number of pilots (and technical officers) had to be promoted to take over the management and command of the Air Force and its formations many of which had to be raised from the ground upward since almost all the bases and training facilities of pre-independence India, had now become part of Pakistan.

The first trainer built in post-independence HAL was manufactured under licence, though in small numbers. The single-engine, low wing Percival Prentice monoplane with fixed undercarriage of all-metal construction powered by a Gypsy Queen 71 engine of 345 hp was regarded as an appropriate basic trainer for the Indian Air Force and also offered HAL a good stepping stone to build manufacturing capacity. The programme was logical, with HAL to assemble the first 15 aircraft from sub-assemblies supplied by the UK company in Luton (five from detailed parts, while the balance 45 aircraft would be built from raw material). Thus, 65 Prentices were delivered to the IAF from April 1948 onwards, the order being completed by 1949. The first Prentice assembled by HAL flew on April 30, 1948, and, according to HAL's chief test pilot. Captain Jimmy Munshi, "had remarkably few snags after its first test flight..... which augurs well for the future."[12]

The First Indigenous Design: HT-2 Basic Trainer
During 1947-48, there were discussions and deliberations on the practicability of establishing such a nucleus of the Aircraft

Design Division. These dragged on for over a year before positive decisions were taken but then came the question: "what type of aircraft is to be designed first?" Concurrently with the licensed manufacture of the Prentice, an Aircraft Design & Development Department was established in HAL at Bangalore, with Dr.V.M. Ghatage as its first head. Dr Ghatage, thus, became India's first aircraft designer, who then joined the IISc (Indian Institute of Science), Bangalore, in 1942, in its formative years, and later did his structural engineering at Gottingen in Germany. To him is owed a great deal for firmly laying the foundations for indigenous aircraft design and development. The first *de-novo* aircraft design and development programme was the "Hindustan Trainer No. 2" or HT-2, which soon became well known in India as the first aircraft to be "designed, developed and manufactured in India by Indians and for Indians".

Different people had different ideas, but it was wisely agreed to first go for a primary trainer for pilot training with both the Indian Air Force as well as civilian flying clubs. The decision was officially conveyed on October 11, 1948, along with the sanction of funds by the Government of India. The government had actually cleared HAL to proceed with the development of three aircraft types: the HT-2 as the primary trainer, the HT-10 advanced trainer, and HT-11 as the intermediate trainer (the latter to replace the T-6G Texan/Harvard with the IAF). However, limited infrastructure and new commitments to manufacture the Vampire jet fighters under licence led to rethinking on further development of the HT-10 and HT-11 trainers beyond the mock-up state in the early Fifties. The Indian government had invited Professor Willy Messerschmitt, the German designer of the legendary Me-109s and Me-262s, to come to India and advise on the future of the national aircraft industry. He had presented a comprehensive report in which was outlined the industrial base that he considered necessary on which to establish a sound aircraft industry. As per the official history of HAL, Professor Messerschmitt's suggestions were not acted upon "partly because of the tautly-stretched Indian economy and partly as a result of inadequate appreciation by the Indian government of probable future requirements,"[13] and the lack of an adequate infrastructure was, as foreseen by Messerschmitt, to inhibit the Indian aircraft industry and delay development. But HAL did go on to manufacture the Vampire jet fighter under licence, the first three aircraft arriving in New Delhi on November 4, 1948.

Design work on the HT-2 began almost straightaway and the full-scale wooden mock-up was completed by August 1949. The design was submitted for a critical review by representatives of the Directorate General of Civil Aviation (DGCA), Indian Air Force and civil flying clubs, and the design and performance aspects deliberated upon before general approval was accorded with some slight modifications. The designers and prototype shop staff worked in close liaison, energised also by the honour of working on this, India's very own aircraft design.

The first flight of the prototype, VT-DFW, took place on August 5, 1951, by Captain J.K. Munshi, which was a defining moment for HAL and the country. Munshi's enthusiasm was such that on the very first flight which lasted 55 minutes, he carried out almost all possible manoeuvres, stalls, loops, spins and dives, all very spectacular, but unusual!

The HT-2 was put on public display at the Bangalore factory on August 13, 1951, for which the Defence Secretary H.M. Patel, and Air Vice Marshal Subroto Mukerjee, the then Deputy Chief of the Air Staff, flanked by HAL's General Manager M.K. Sen Gupta and Dr. V.M. Ghatage were amongst the 1,000-odd invitees. The HT-2 was flight demonstrated by Captain Munshi.

Aircraft design requires extensive trials under test flights to ensure that the aircraft meets all specifications set for, and by, the designers. Hence the HT-2, flying well, especially in the hands of experienced pilots, was one thing, and its performance under other circumstances, especially by rookie pilots, would have to be ensured to make it at a very minimum, safe, and capable of the missions it was designed for. Unfortunately, when spinning trials were commenced on the HT-2, it was found that it was prone to enter into flat spin and not recoverable without the use of full power. Modifications made it worse and in the following sortie, the aircraft did not respond to the recovery actions after three turns and developed a flat spin even after application of full power. As there was no anti-spin parachute fitted, the prototype was perforce abandoned after about 14 turns, the test pilot descending by parachute, and the aircraft was destroyed. It was recommended that the fin, rudder and horizontal tail areas be increased and the latter repositioned. With this modification, the spinning characteristics were entirely satisfactory, and the second prototype, VT-DGG, which was first flown on February 19, 1952, followed by its development test flights, now fully safe to handle, continued as per schedule. Complete flight testing of the HT-2 was entrusted to Squadron Leader Suranjan Das (who had been seconded to HAL in June 1951), unquestionably one of India's most brilliant test pilots, and whose name will forever be synonymous with HAL.

After preliminary flights on the HT-2 in August 1951, work started in earnest to make a complete quantitative and qualitative assessment of the HT-2's stability and control characteristics and also of its performance and landing. It was first necessary to prove that the HT-2 was safe before other tests of less importance could be carried out. Squadron Leader Suranjan Das completed all HT-2 test flying with the comment that the "HT-2 is a very strong and aerodynamically satisfactory aircraft.... safety and controllability are quite adequate. The cost of operation would also compare favourably with current trainer aircraft. Much knowledge was gained through development flying but there had been a number of failures too, very common in this game, as each failure adds to the knowledge of both the 'boffin' and the 'airframe driver' which are there for keeps". The official Type Certificate was formally awarded to the HT-2 on January 3, 1953, and later in the month, the first batch of six HT-2s was flown to Palam (Delhi) for display and demonstration but the type was officially introduced as an elementary trainer to replace the Tiger Moth with the IAF only from January 10, 1955. The HT-2 became primary flying equipment at the Flight Instructors School at Tambaram and No. 2 Air Force Academy, Begumpet, where pupil pilots logged some 75 hours on the type before advancing to Harvard intermediate trainers. Post 1962, as the Indian Air Force was to be expanded manifold, the HT-2s from Auxiliary Air Force Squadrons and most of the civil flying clubs were taken over and, supplemented by aircraft from other IAF training units, were assigned to the Pilot Training Establishment (PTE) at Allahabad. In 1966, the PTE was relocated at Bidar (in Karnataka) and renamed as the Elementary Flying School (EFS).

A good number of these were built by HAL, powered by the Cirrus Major III of 155 hp, production terminating in 1958. The only real export order was from the Ghana Air Force which purchased twelve HT-2s in 1959.[14] Air HQ had finalised the requirement of replacement for the HT-2 in 1969 to be designed as early as possible because of increasing unreliability of the engine and numerous accidents; and the Chief of the Air Staff (now Marshal of the IAF, Arjan Singh DFC, had noted on the file that we should consider powering the aircraft with a turbo-engine. However, the aircraft continued in service with the IAF till around 1984 after some of these aircraft were re-engined with the Avco Lycoming AEIO-320-D2B of 160 hp in 1981 before the HPT-32 started to replace it. The reasons for the delay in designing an early replacement are not clear, at least in the public information domain. But it is generally believed that the DGCA in collaboration with IIT, New Delhi, had started to design a trainer which was claimed to be able to fulfil all the training requirements of the IAF, civil needs and the flying clubs.

HPT-32 Trainer

It took HAL nearly a decade to design and produce the replacement in the shape of the HPT-32 in 1977 since the government had decided that we must await the outcome of the trainer being designed by DGCA and IIT, New Delhi! Incidentally, the DGCA is the regulatory authority for civil aviation and it is not clear how and why it had entered into aircraft design while the nominated institution, HAL, was short of work and the IAF was struggling with the ageing HT-2. Ultimately, the DGCA design proved grossly inadequate and work on the HAL trainer for the IAF started. But even here, HAL included into the design requirements features to enable the small aircraft to be able to carry four persons (including the pilot) so that the aircraft could be used for communication duties even in the private sector!

However, the HPT-32 was not cleared by IAF test pilots for induction into the IAF since it did not satisfy the ASR (Air Staff Requirements) in respect on US Mil Specs because the rate of spinning was very high. The Chief of the Air Staff, conscious of the grim situation where basic flying training had lost its orientation and goals, asked the Chairman of the La Fontaine Committee (looking into aircraft accidents) and two other highly qualified and experienced pilot instructors to go down to Bangalore, fly the prototypes and report to him. They were unanimous in their conclusions that, in the absence of any possibility of importing a primary trainer, the aircraft was acceptable for induction and replacement of the HT-2. One of them had put down in his report that the HPT-32 was underpowered and, hence, the pupil would get less instructional time in the air and the engine would be strained by longer use of full throttle in climbing back after almost every aerobatic manoeuvre. Based on this minority view, HAL, on the directions of its new Chairman, Air Marshal L.M. Katre, immediately after he took over, did produce a modified aircraft with a turbo-prop engine called the HTT-34 which was apparently quite satisfactory and used the main of the airframe of the HPT-32 with the tail unit modified. It is not clear why this was not inducted into the Air Force then, or for that matter in 2009 when all HPT-32s had to be grounded because of serious engine trouble, fatal accidents, and basic flying training in the Air Force was completely disrupted to the extent that the government had to float a Request for Information (RFI) for possible purchase of new primary trainers from abroad — a most serious indictment of HAL and its inability to meet even the light trainer aircraft requirements of the IAF more than seven decades after HAL came into being.

HAL's HAOP-27 Krishak

It needs to be recalled that HAL, instead of designing and manufacturing the H-10 and H-11, undertook the development of a light two-seat cabin monoplane to meet the requirements of Indian flying clubs (that were already being supplied with HT-2 aircraft), initiating construction on August

7, 1958, as a private venture and flying the prototype less than two months later, on September 28. Powered by a 90 bhp Continental "flat-four" piston engine, the HUL-26 Pushpak, as the light aeroplane was designated, proved itself a rugged little monoplane with pleasant handling characteristics and an acceptable performance. Also, in 1958, work on a more powerful four-seat multi-purpose derivative of the Pushpak, known as the Krishak, began, the first of two prototypes flying in November 1959. Although not developed for the civil roles originally envisaged, this aircraft was adapted for the Army's Air Observation Post (AOP) role and, as a two/three-seater with a 225 hp Continental 0-470-J "flat-six", entered production for the Indian Air Force as the HAOP-27 Krishak after a prototype had been flown in 1965 and served well.

This development took place since after the 1962 Sino-Indian War, the Indian armed forces were to be expanded and the Army, including the Regiment of Artillery, equipped to fight both on the plains and in the mountains. The Air OP component was to be greatly expanded and as a replacement to the Auster AOP-9, the indigenous HAOP-27 Krishak was suitably developed. As noted above, work on a more powerful four-seat multi-purpose development of the two-seat Pushpak had been initiated by HAL in 1958 and the prototype first flown in November 1959. Development of an AOP, liaison and ambulance variant of the basic Krishak design was carried out with the prototype (BR 464) which flew in 1965.

Stressed to a limiting load factor of 3.8 g, the military version was given the nomenclature HAOP-27 (Hindustan Air Observation Post–27) and was powered by a Continental "flat six" engine of 225 hp The initial order for Krishaks was placed on HAL with deliveries commencing in late 1965 and a subsequent order for more in 1966 resulted in a number of

AOP Squadrons and Independent Flights being established, conversion training being provided on the type at Patiala. These squadrons were commanded by a Lieutenant Colonel of the Regiment of the Artillery, with the Adjutant seconded by the Air Force, and the IAF remained responsible for the aircraft's serviceability, maintenance and allotment although operational use and control was directed by the Army.

The Krishak's predecessor, the ultra light HUL-26 two-seat Pushpak, had also donned military colours during the 1965 operations against Pakistan, the aircraft being "borrowed" from civil flying clubs, and "militarised". With availability of the Krishaks, the AOP units were able to operate a more suitable aircraft and the HAOP-27 served in all sectors of the western front during the December 1971 conflict, providing invaluable direction to the gunners in the face of strong enemy air and ground reaction. During the famous Battle of Longewala on December 4-5, 1971, west of Jaisalmer, when IAF Hunters destroyed a regiment of Pakistani tanks and associated vehicles belonging to the Pakistan Army's 18 Division, Major (later Major General) Atma Singh of AOP, flying a Krishak guided numerous Hunter strikes against the tanks, continuing to do so even after his aircraft engine was hit by Pakistani ground fire and he had to carry out a forced landing in the battle zone. Atma Singh was awarded a Vir Chakra by the Air Force, and the aircraft was later retrieved from the battlefield.

For air observation and light utility tasks in the mountains, however, there was rethinking on employment of fixed-wing aircraft as helicopters would be far more versatile, operating, as they could, from advance helipads. In the late Seventies, the Krishaks were supplanted by HAL Cheetah helicopters.

HA-31 Mk.II Basant

Aircraft were first used in India for pest control in 1944, when a Hurricane IIC of the IAF was employed to spray chemicals against locust swarms in the Rajasthan desert. In 1956, sugarcane crops were sprayed for the control of pyrilla pests and, encouraged by the results, the Ministry of Agriculture established an aerial unit under the Directorate of Plant Protection in 1959, which eventually became the Directorate of Agricultural Aviation in 1971. It was felt that the use of aircraft as a part of the integrated farm economy was a measure needed to generate more food and fibre in the quickest possible time. By 1974, as many as 14 Indian companies, mostly private, were active with 28 fixed-wing aircraft and 25 helicopters, all modified for carrying out spraying.

Hindustan Aeronautics Limited got down to designing an agricultural aircraft but the initial effort was not considered suitable (the Basant Mk. I) and so the Mk. II was developed, which was a strut-braced, low-wing monoplane with fixed tail and wheel type undercarriage. Powered by an Avco-Lycoming 10-720-CIB engine of 400 hp, with the Hartzell three-bladed constant speed propeller, the Basant had a fabric-covered, tubular welded fuselage but the tailplane, wing leading edges and forward fuselage which housed the engine and the 33 cu.ft. fibre-glass hopper, were metal reinforced. Its forward location also provided adequate protection for the pilot as also pitch-up motion, during dumping.

The HA-31 Mk.II Basant ("Spring" in Punjabi) was designed, developed and built by HAL in 15 months, the first prototype (VT-XAO) first flying on April 30, 1972, with its DGCA Type Certificate received in January 1974 and orders for a large number placed by the Ministry of Agriculture in August 1974 which had loaned Rs. 15 million to HAL for development. The

first five Basants were handed over by M.M. Sen, Chairman of
HAL, to the Union Ministry of Agriculture on June 21, 1974,
the aircraft received by Group Captain S.P. Sen, Director of
Agricultural Aviation who was thereafter replaced by Group
Captain S. "Chacha" Sahni. In the very first season of their
deployment, in 1975-76, the Basants proved their sturdiness
and capacity by undertaking an average of 30 sorties a day, and
spraying over 2,000 acres each, a record of 39 sorties being
achieved by one particular Basant which sprayed 3,315 acres
in a day.

However, agricultural aviation soon came under strict
regulatory control from 1976, covering pilot licences,
operators, monitoring of chemicals used, enhanced flight
safety (potential hazards for the low flying operations) and
restriction on the number of hours flown to compensate
for pilot fatigue. The state of Haryana became the first
to unreservedly back the HAL-developed aircraft by
placing orders for five Basants. Under the direction of Air
Commodore N.P. Nair, Civil Aviation Adviser, Haryana Agro
Aviation pioneered the operating procedures, supported at
each step by HAL and clearly demonstrated that the Basant
was an entirely sound design, capable of carrying out spraying
operations under rudimentary field conditions.

In mid-June 1975, the Basants were ferried from Bangalore
to Pinjore, a small airfield north of the Shivaliks and within
a fortnight began aerial spraying of cotton crops in the
Hissar district. The Basants came out with "flying colours",
operating from both Hissar and a *kutcha* airstrip at Ratia.
With uncertainties of HS-748 production continuing at HAL
Kanpur, a policy decision was taken to transfer the HA-31
Basant Mk.II production line to Kanpur. Thirteen Basants
had been produced by this time and the 20th and last pre-

production aircraft was delivered in March 1975. The next
11 Basants were built at Kanpur making a total of 31 Basant
Mk.IIs built. The other HAL-manufactured aircraft to be used
for agricultural purposes was a modified SA 315B Cheetah
helicopter, fitted with spraying equipment and hopper tanks
on either sides and behind the cabin, each having a capacity of
150 Imperial Gallons (Imp Gal).

HJT-16 Kiran – The Intermediate Jet Trainer

The first jet aircraft to be designed and developed and
manufactured by HAL was the HJT-16 given the Indian name
of "Kiran." The need for an intermediate trainer to eventually
replace the T-6G Texan (or Harvard) piston-engine trainer of
the Indian Air Force was first mooted in 1958 and HAL was
officially given the "go-ahead" for design and development of
such an aircraft in December 1959. Under the leadership of
Dr. V M Ghatage, HAL's Chief Designer, a team of engineers
initiated work from July 1960, and from April 1961, under
Raj Mahindra, then Senior Design Engineer, that work gained
momentum. By September 1961, the design group had
increased to 23 personnel, growing to 46 by mid-1962 and 55
by mid-1963. The design staff were drawn from the limited
numbers available, with priority being assigned to the HF-24
project and at the peak, the strength of the HJT-16 design
group, including design engineers, tracers and secretarial staff,
reached 94 excluding personnel at the prototype shop. There
is some record that a peak figure of 90 designers was achieved
by July 1960.[15]

There was close interaction between the designers at
HAL and the main stakeholder, the Indian Air Force. The
IAF Training Command set up an AF Project Team at HAL
as did the DTD&P (Air), the HJT-16 full-scale wooden mock-

up being subjected to continuous review. Three wind-tunnel models, two of wood and to ¼ and ½ scale, and one of light alloy were fabricated and low speed tests conducted at the Indian Institute of Science's 14'x9' low- speed wind tunnel during February 1962-July 1963. High-speed tests were done at the 8'x6' Transonic Wind Tunnel at the Royal Aircraft Establishment, Farnborough, in September 1962, even as various structural tests using specimen parts such as ribs, inter-spar box, nose ribs and root fitting, were carried out in the Prototype Development Shop and central laboratory at HAL, Bangalore. The HJT-16 design was frozen, mock-up fabricated and aerodynamic tests completed by December 1962 even as Air Headquarters assessed the side-by-side seating arrangement of the cockpit but the mock-up could not be fully completed because the allotted funds had "run out" by 1963! Nevertheless, as portions of the mock-up were readied and as details were finalised, initial prototype production drawings were issued from mid-1962, further drawings being continuously issued till the end of 1963 and were completed by early 1964.

Early in the project, it had been decided to develop the tooling for prototypes which could also be used for the first batch of pre-production aircraft, so saving time and cost. In February 1963, work on major assembly jigs was started and completed in nine months. The close coordination among the prototype, planning and design group paid dividends as at no stage were there any hold-ups for want of materials. As it was decided not to use forgings for the prototype, all fittings were made of bar stock. Fabrication orders were released for 3 sets of all details and minor sub-assemblies except in the case of long cycle parts and although this approach delayed the first prototype to an extent, it advanced the date of assembly of the second prototype and test specimen. With work beginning in January 1963, detailed parts for the first prototype were completed in August 1964 and now events moved rapidly. By the end of 1963, some of the senior staff on the HF-24 project also become available on a "part time basis" and so increasingly equipment and installation drawings were released between March 1964 and August 1964. The first prototype was rolled out of the shop for weighing and final checks on August 26, 1964, the first engine ground run (the Viper II Mk.22-8 turbojet of 2,500 lb.s.t.) carried out on August 28, 1964, and taxi trials started in September 1964. The maiden flight of the first prototype of the HJT-16 (U 327) with Group Captain Suranjan Das at the controls took place on September 4, 1964.

Development work on the Kiran was somewhat extended, mainly because of its failure to meet the ASR with its stall warning speed too close to stall. Various methods to increase the stall warning period were explored, and development was finally completed only by 1970, by which time a number of pre-production aircraft had been produced. The Indian Air Force had placed orders for these aircraft in March 1963, adding up with the order in batches from 1965 to 1974 (including a batch for the Indian Navy). The production rate which was 7 aircraft in 1970-71, started to pick up and from 11 Kirans in 1971-72, went up to 20 Kirans in 1973-74, peaking at 22 aircraft in 1975-76, and the total order for aircraft was completed by March 31, 1982.

The development of an armed version, designated as the Kiran Mk.IA was taken up and completed in 1974, the performance being essentially similar to the Mk.I except for the carriage of underwing armament stores on two hard points (mid-line gun pods, rocket pods or bombs). The 116th production aircraft onwards were made to the Kiran Mk.IA standard. Generations of IAF pilots have flown and trained on the Kiran jet trainer and the type has served the air arm well. An experienced Qualified Flying Instructor (QFI) described the Kiran successfully, "When one approaches the HJT-16 Kiran, what strikes one is its purposeful and robust appearance, looks endorsed in actual experience by its capacity to effectively withstand a great deal of mishandling and even inevitable abuse by fledgling pilots under training. The canopy is hinged at the rear and can be jettisoned independently. The cockpit has a functional look with the instruments, controls, switches and warning indicators neatly arranged within easy reach." In fact, the human engineering department of the IAF's Institute of Aviation Medicine, located close to the HAL factory, was intimately involved in cockpit design and layout of the Kiran. Unfortunately, the cockpit space is limited and pilots taller than 6 feet rarely qualify in view of the rather tight stringent requirements of sitting height, leg length, etc.

There is an apparent contradiction that has never been addressed. Till HAL got down to designing the HF-24, the only aircraft it had designed was the primary trainer, the HT-2 and the two light aircraft, the Pushpak and the Krishak. No doubt, it had started manufacturing the well-tested de Havilland Vampire (more of it later) and was beginning to develop and manufacture the Folland Gnat, both under licence and, no doubt, gave tremendous experience to the fledgling aircraft factory. But to have started the design and development of the ambitious programme of a multi-role combat aircraft like the HF-24 (though the collaborative design team was led by the Germans), and to concurrently commence design and development of the intermediate jet trainer, the HJT-16, appears incongruous and obviously overstretching the limited capability and even less experience. Contrary to some views, the HJT-16 was not meant to be the replacement for the Vampire (trainer and fighter combination) being used in what is well known across the world as the "lead-in fighter" trainer role, in those years being undertaken at the OTU (Operational Training Unit) at Hakimpet, north edge of Secunderabad. The Vampires were expected to be phased out by 1972-73. The only possible explanation of the flurry of designs in HAL with its limited capacity for such things since late the 1950s (till someone can enlighten us with more accurate information) is that the British Royal Air Force had decided around that time to go in for what was termed as the "all-through jet training scheme." The IAF also planned to go in for a similar scheme; hence, there was little interest in replacing the HT-2 (till the 1970s) since by the early 1960s, the RAF had given up the all-through jet training scheme as costly and unsuitable. Even the IAF had given up the idea of such a scheme, but only after importing the Polish made Iskara trainers to boost the strength of jet aircraft at the intermediate stage. Somewhere along the line, the necessity of the "lead-in fighter" trainer was lost on the then policy-makers.

Well after the retirement of the Vampire T.55 side-seating jet trainers with the Indian Air Force, and the lack of a platform for weapons delivery training, the Kiran Mk.II was conceived. A derivative of the basic trainer, the aircraft was to incorporate eight modifications, the most critical being reengining with an Orpheus 701 (derated to 3,500 lb.s.t). The unpretentious Orpheus turbojet engine had been built in quantity by HAL's Engine Division for the Gnat and Marut programmes and after the in-service life of the latter had been prematurely shortened, a large number of Orpheus engines were available.

Augmentation of the thrust by nearly 50 percent gave the Kiran Mk.II considerable additional power and, hence, the capability to carry extra underwing stores at four hard points with universal ejection pylons, at a maximum all-up-weight of 5,000 kg. Two integral guns, each of 7.62mm calibre were installed in the forward fuselage, and HAL manufactured-Ferranti ISIS gunsights made available to each of the two side-by-side seated pilots. The aircraft was fitted with the latest avionics and instruments, all designed and manufactured indigenously at HAL's various complexes, including Martin Baker ground-level ejection seats for both pilots. The internal fuel capacity of 1,340 litres was augmented by 20 per cent and external fuel carried in four drop tanks of 225 litre capacity each under the wings.

A number of Kiran Mk.IIs were built by HAL's Aircraft Division, all but eight (for the Indian Navy) being delivered to the Indian Air Force, first to the Flying Instructors School at Tambaram and then to the Air Force Academy. In 1992, the year of the IAF's Diamond Jubilee, after the IAF's Thunderbolts acrobatic team had been retired, it was decided to reform an aerobatic team and after some review, the Kiran Mk.II was selected as the mount. Named the Surya Kirans (Rays of the Sun) and painted in resplendent orange colour, the Kiran Mk.IIs have since performed at air shows, parades and other functions throughout the country, so becoming HAL's most public displayed aircraft in its history.

HF-24 "Marut" – India's MRCA

The HF-24 "Marut" combat aircraft was the first indigenously designed combat aircraft that India started at HAL; and the Air Force decided that it should be multi-role twin-engine single-seat combat aircraft capable of Mach-2 as an interceptor while also being capable of ground attack of robust capability. In the mid-1950s, after Pakistan joined the Baghdad Pact and started to receive enormous military aid which on the air force side included squadrons of F-86 Sabre, F-104 Starfighter, and a vast array of radars and communication systems, it became clear that the IAF would have to expand further from the authorised level of 15 squadrons (13 combat squadrons) authorised in 1952. The Tempests and Spitfires, very good aircraft in their time, could not cope with the emerging operational-technological environment, especially since their spare parts were now becoming extremely difficult to procure. The Vampire being produced in the country under licence was no match for what the Pakistan Air Force was acquiring and not enough to meet expansion goals. In fact, the mobilisation and high alert for a war threatened by Liaquat Ali Khan in early 1951 had shown the serious deficiency of the Vampires since critical parts of the guns had not been supplied by the UK. This strengthened the resolve for building self-reliance through diversification as well as indigenisation.

In 1955, Air HQ, with the approval of the Chiefs of Staff Committee, had submitted a case for expansion from 15 to 25 squadrons which in the context of Pakistan's major arms build-up was enhanced to 33 squadrons in 1959.[16] Thus, the requirement of combat aircraft for the IAF in the coming years had to be catered for. One solution was to speed up the development and manufacture of the Gnat aircraft (dealt with later) and the other was outright purchase of combat aircraft from abroad. Both were instituted, with the latter leading to the acquisition of the Mystere IVA and Hunter aircraft. But it was obvious that this would increase India's import dependence and, hence, its security on the policies and interests of other countries. In order to meet the long-term needs of combat aircraft, Air HQ issued an ASR for an advanced combat aircraft which would be employed for both high altitude interception as well as low level ground attack duties. The requirement further specified that it should be possible to develop an advanced trainer, night fighter and 'navalised' version of the basic aircraft. The last requirement appeared curious because India did not possess an aircraft carrier at that time, and the requirement provided a long-term perspective.

This, indeed, was an ambitious goal for a country that had yet to produce even the jet trainer. Conceptually, the Air Force leadership was obviously way ahead of most other countries (with the exception of the US Air Force) that had settled down to role-specific aircraft rather than a Multi-Role Combat Aircraft (MRCA). The UK, from where a great deal of 'wisdom' had continued to flow long after independence, in a wide departure from its Battle of Britain which had saved the country from a German invasion, in fact, decided in its 1957 Defence White Paper that British defence in future would rest, not on manned aircraft, but on missiles! The TSR-2 aircraft programme was cancelled and the only aircraft it produced on its own after that was the Jaguar tactical strike aircraft

In pursuance of the national objective of attaining self-reliance in the design and production of combat aircraft, it was directed that this aircraft be developed within the country. Hindustan Aircraft Limited, as the present Bangalore Division of Hindustan Aeronautics Limited (HAL) was then known, was given the task of preparing itself for the project. HAL was at the time engaged in the manufacture of the Vampire under licence but its design experience was limited to the HT-2 primary trainer. Hence, it was decided to design the new twin-engine aircraft in collaboration with experts from abroad. In August 1956, Dr. Kurt Tank, accompanied by his deputy, Herr Mittelhuber, arrived in Bangalore in response to the invitation to establish and head the design team which would give the ASR shape and substance.

Although HAL was immersed in a number of production programmes, there were only three senior Indian design engineers and an infant design department whose total strength was 54. The prototype shop had a complement of some 60 men, including supervisors, while 13 men constituted the entire strength of the production engineering department. The entire infrastructure had to be built up from the grassroots. Raju Thomas wrote that "the Germans worked mainly on their own, and did not train a succeeding team of Indian engineers when they left."[17] However, the truth was that by the time of the HF-24's first flight, Dr. Tank had, in addition to 18 German design engineers, *a design department of 150 Indians,* the prototype shop having increased its personnel strength to 592 workers and 59 supervisors while the production engineering department boasted of over 100 engineers/technicians. The problems of the HF-24 and any follow-on designs, as we shall see shortly, lay elsewhere. This also must be seen in the context of the output from the Indian Institute of Science being a mere 20 per year of whom more than half went abroad or pursued basic research in the laboratories of CSIR.

Design work commenced in June 1957. Later that year, Dr. Kurt Tank and his senior German and Indian colleagues visited Kalaikunda Air Force Station in order to have a closer look at the Mystere IVA based there since the weapons and weapon aiming systems/parameters specified for the HF-24 were practically the same. The Mystere was undoubtedly the most heavily armed combat aircraft in the IAF till it acquired the Su-30. The HF-24 carried a pack of 68mm rockets in the belly (which could be alternated with an auxiliary fuel tank to increase internal fuel) besides the external four pods of 16 rockets of 68mm calibre like the Mystere IVA. The Mystere gunsight with radar ranging was also adapted for the HF-24.

In the spirit of enthusiasm that such a pioneering effort generated, the work was completed rapidly, the final mock-up conference, finalising requirements around the full scale wooden layout simulating the aerodynamic envelope being held ten months later on April 10, 1958. In the absence of adequate wind tunnels and in keeping with the style preferred by German fighter designers in those years, a full scale wooden glider was constructed and glider trials were initiated on April 1, 1959, the test pilots involved at this stage being Wing Commanders Roshan Suri and Kapil Bhargava. As the glider was a two-seater (in tandem), Dr. Kurt Tank was able to make a couple of flights himself as an observer, the rear seat otherwise housing test equipment and a remotely controlled camera focussed on the rear instrument panel. The HF-24 glider towed by a C-47 and usually released from between 12,000 to 15,000 ft, last flew on March 24, 1960, having completed a total of 78 flights devoted largely to low speed handling characteristics.

Assembly of the first prototype (HF 001) began in April 1960 and, eleven months later, on March 11, 1961, taxi trials under power commenced. For three months, the prototype underwent a comprehensive ground-test programme, including an involved testing of systems, functioning of controls, air brakes, flaps, steering, cockpit escape drills, brake performance, etc. The old humped runway at the HAL airport, Bangalore, had by this time been supplemented by a 10,850 ft runway and the first flight of the HF-24 was carried out on June 17, 1961, four years after the design process commenced. Wing Commander Suranjan Das was at the controls. The first official flight took place a week later, on June 24, 1961, the prototype, now sporting IAF roundels and the serial BR 462, giving an half hour flying display in the presence of the then Defence Minister, V.K. Krishna Menon, and a large number of defence and media invitees.

By November 1961, a structural test airframe had been completed and this was subjected to extensive structural and functional tests in rigs designed and fabricated at Bangalore. The airframe underwent ground resonance, material property and endurance tests, under simulated inertia loads, which led to destructive testing while a nose-section was fitted out for armament trials. As the rig tests and flight testing of individual, components progressed, the BR 462 was joined by the second prototype aircraft (BR 463) which first flew on October 4, 1962, and flight development continued with Group Captain Suranjan Das as the Chief Test Pilot, Wing Commanders (then Squadron Leaders) Inder Chopra being largely involved with stability trials, W.M. "ChuChu" Tilak with the armament and instrumentation work and 'Babi' Dey with power plant trials, the last three mentioned being IAF test pilots on loan to HAL. The BR-463 featured a repositioned pitot head boom and incorporated a tail brake-parachute to assist in slowing down after landing.

Marut's Achilles' Heel
The Marut's Achilles' heel was its engine where a fundamental principle that you design an aircraft around a (proven) engine and not the other way round, had been violated. It was claimed that the Marut airframe could accept five types of engines. But it finally remained in service with the very first interim engine, the Bristol 703, which left the aircraft grossly underpowered at lower speeds and higher altitudes. While it must be admitted that there was a number of unexpected coincidences, the basic fact was that in principle, the planning was wrong, and in practice flawed, especially in the failure to fund the development of the B.Or12 in spite of the fact that the stakes were so high. The tragedy is that we did not the learn the lessons right and

made the same mistake with the Light Combat Aircraft (LCA), India's next indigenously designed combat aircraft, after a gap of three decades!

When it started to fly, the HF-24 Marut attracted world attention with wonder, disbelief and jealousy. It was only a few years earlier that the British (including the British Chief of Staff of the IAF) were saying that Indian pilots would not be able to fly the French fighter, Dassault Ouragon (christened Toofani in India) and would meet with many accidents. They were proved wrong when four brand new aircraft were ferried from France to New Delhi without any incident in 1953; and later in 1955, Marshal of the IAF Arjan Singh (then an Air Commodore) led an eight-aircraft formation of Toofani fighters to Rangoon on a goodwill mission on the 10th anniversary of the liberation of Burma from Japanese occupation in the battle in which the IAF had played a crucial role. And now the Marut, with a small German-led Indian team of designers and Indian test pilots was promising to be the world's most remarkable multi-role combat aircraft. The Achilles' heel was the power plant.

As noted above, HAL was under the Ministry of Industries and Supplies (as in the UK) until 1958 when it was brought under the Ministry of Defence like the rest of the defence industry, along with the Controller General of Defence Production. By 1958, Dr. D.S. Kothari was appointed as the full time Scientific Adviser to the Defence Ministry and later to the Defence Minister to advise on matters related to defence science and research and development, and the CCR&D was brought under the Scientific Adviser in contradiction to the global norm that kept the scientists in the advisory role and not in executive positions. The then CCR&D, Major General B.D. Kapur was to write later that "none of the SAs (Scientific Advisers) in the USA, Canada or British accepted any load of administrative responsibility."[18]

The basic HF-24 design had been planned on two 3,700 kg.s.t. each afterburning Bristol Orpheus B.Or.12 engines which were originally being developed for the North Atlantic Treaty Organisation (NATO) light-weight strike fighter and the supersonic Gnat Mk.II interceptor. By 1959, however, further development of the engine was in jeopardy when British authorities confirmed that they had no requirement for the power plant after the Gnat Mk.II was cancelled along with the TSR-2. Bristol offered to complete the development of the B.Or 12 if the Government of India was willing to pay the costs involved. The development costs were quoted as GBP 3 million.[19] At the then currency exchange rates this amounted to approximately Rs. 4 crore, no doubt payable over a couple of years, linked to development processes. However, South Block in its wisdom or otherwise believed that this was excessive. The amount quoted by Bristol, with its high reputation in engine design and development, and whose Orpheus 703 was being used in the HF-24 Mk.I, for development of the Bristol B.Or12 amounted to 0.0048 percent of the defence budget of 1963-64, and equal to the cost of 4-5 Marut aircraft;[20] but would no doubt have to be paid out over a couple of years! South Block apparently turned down the proposal on the grounds of expense, ultimately spending far more money (including foreign exchange) in the wild goose chase for engines and local development.

Group Captain Jacob Chakko, an outstanding technical officer of the IAF, who also was a flyer, in his *Memoirs*, writes:[21]

> The choice of engines (for HF-24) got quickly mired in the politics of the day. The choices available were many. Rolls Royce had one of the best but the French SNECMA and the Russian RD9F were also in the running. There were definitely good arguments as to why such a jet engine should be an indigenous design, capable of being developed by

our own engineers and manufactured by the HAL Engine Factory. But it soon became a choice between the then Defence Minister's (Krishna Menon) preference for a Soviet engine and the Air HQ's preference for a British or French one.

This left the HAL design team with little choice but to adopt the unreheated Orpheus 703, developing 2,200 kg as the power plant for the interim Mark I. According to the 1966 Education Commission, the average allocation for R&D in India before 1960 was about 0.1 percent of the Gross National Product (GNP).[22] (It still continues at less than 0.8 percent of the Gross Domestic Prodcut – GDP.) The capacity of indigenous development in a country long deindustrialised to produce a reheated jet engine of high efficiency and power output was questionable to start with. The Indian government took a decision, late in 1962, that rather than postpone further development and manufacture, some pre-production aircraft followed by a batch of series-production Mark Is would be ordered. Simultaneously began the search for an alternate power plant. In 1961, the Russian government was approached with the Klimov VK-7 turbojet in mind and several engines were subjected to evaluation tests. The centrifugal flow VK-7 could not, however, be fitted to the existing HF-24 airframe without major design changes; and attention shifted to the RD-9F axial flow engine (fitted on the MiG-19), eight of which were imported in late 1961 and bench-tested at Bangalore. Negotiations for the licensed manufacture of this Russian engine were discontinued under the instruction of Air Vice Marshal Ranjan Dutt, Chairman HAL, at the beginning of 1964, for reasons difficult to fathom at this stage. The engines gifted by the Soviet Union were, instead, transferred to Tambaram for technical airmen's training.

An alternate was considered in the shape of the E-300 turbojet, designed by Dipl. Ing. Ferdinand Brandner, in

Germany against an Egyptian contract. A relatively simple lightweight turbojet with a 9-stage compressor and a 2-stage turbine, it was considered that a smaller afterburner version, the EI-300 with reheat, could be developed for the HF-24. The collaboration agreement was signed in Cairo on November 2, 1964. The Indian government sought to get the engine at location in HAL where the Gas Turbine Research Establishment (GTRE) expertise would also be available. But Egypt refused and finally the Indian government furnished, in July 1965, a specially modified pre-production Marut given the type designation HF-24 Mk.IBX, and seconding two test pilots, Wing Commander Kapil Bhargava (who was then Chief Test Pilot with the Messerschmitt designed HA-300 flight test programme) and Squadron Leader Inder Chopra, plus maintenance crew. The modified Marut had a redesigned fuselage able to accommodate either the Orpheus 703 or E-300 but form drag was considerable. The HF-24 initially retained one of its two Orpheus 703s and a total flying time of 106 hours was completed on 150 flights and up to an altitude of 26,000 ft. Flight testing was satisfactory but after the June 1967 Arab-Israeli War, development work was reduced drastically and the Indian team had virtually little to do.

Late in 1964 there was a lukewarm Bristol Siddeley proposal to employ the high pressure inner spool of the Pegasus married to the HAL-produced Orpheus 703, thereby theoretically offering a similar performance to that of the abandoned B.Or12; but this was not progressed, for reasons difficult to fathom. Instead, as an indigenous exercise, the Indian government directed that the development of an afterburner for the Orpheus 703, be undertaken by the GTRE at Bangalore. Aiming for 36 percent boost in reheat thrust, design of an afterburning system progressed and in 1964, an 18 percent boost in thrust was achieved.

The first Marut with reheat, a modified Mark I, was the HF 005 and this flying test-bed was known as the Mk.IA. Initially scheduled to fly in late 1964, acceptance trials were not entirely satisfactory and, in fact, it was only in September 1966 that the Defence Ministry announced that the reheat Marut prototypes had initiated test flights. By 1970, two Mk.IIs and the Mk.IA were involved in the reheat development trials at which time the Orpheus 703 afterburning system had progressed to provide a 27 percent boost (to 6,160 Ib.s.t.). The simplified reheat system designed by the Gas Turbine Research Establishment, operated at 1700° K and since the Orpheus 703 is a low pressure ratio engine, the thrust increment with reheat was limited to 27 percent. Development flying of the Marut with reheat suffered a severe setback when, on January 10, 1970, the prototype Mk.IR flown by Group Captain Suranjan Das, tragically crashed just after take-off, India's finest test pilot being killed in the accident. It is believed in some quarters that the mistake was in the design of the GTRE reheat component in "not adding to the afterburner a by-pass to provide additional air for the required mass" leading to the explosion of the engine and the aircraft.[23]

The RD 172/T. 260 Adour reheat twin spool turbofan was considered intermittently for some years by the Indian government, with negotiations beginning in 1970. However, the Indian Air Force would only consider placing an order for the Marut Mk.II (as the production Mk.IR was to be known) if a modified and further augmented (by 20) Adour was made available. Meanwhile, the first pre-production HF-24 Mk.I had made its initial flight in April 1964 and was joined by two more within the year. Two of these were handed over by the then

Managing Director (MD) of HAL, Air Vice Marshal Ranjan
Dutt to the CAS, Air Marshal A.M. Engineer at a ceremony
on May 10, 1964, at Bangalore. The aircraft, now named the
Marut, or the *"Spirit of Tempest and Thunder"*, were taken over by
the IAF's Aircraft and Armament Testing Unit, (A & ATU), an
organisation evaluating aircraft and weapon systems at Kanpur.
Joined by increasing numbers of pre-production aircraft, they
underwent service and weapon system trials (the latter at the
Armament Training Wing) for nearly three years, leading to
the establishment of the IAF's first squadron equipped with
the Marut, on April 1, 1967.

Of the pre-production aircraft ordered, three were retained
by HAL for equipment and avionics development work, two
became experimental prototypes fitted with the reheat system,
one was involved with the Egyptian E-300 engine project, the
balance being handed over to the Indian Air Force. A close
liaison was developed between the IAF and HAL during
the period of service evaluation, aircraft being updated and
modified as dictated by the Air Force's low level ground attack-
profile requirement, envisaged for fulfilment by the Marut
Mk.I, and weapon systems and avionics suitably selected.

All major flight testing had been completed prior to the
handing over of the pre-production aircraft to the IAF and
some 1,800 test flights carried out by the time the first series
production Mark I aircraft flew on November 15, 1967. The
development phases of the HF-24 were fairly uneventful and
gave little trouble. By and large, the original design concepts
proved themselves and there were no major problems which
may have necessitated a major redesigning in the structure or
systems. Although the Marut had fine aerodynamic qualities,
drag reduction studies continued as did flight testing of new
systems desired by the IAF.

After the flight of the first pre-production aircraft, the number of Germans on the design staff was progressively reduced, down to ten in 1964 and only Dr. Kurt Tank was left by 1965, the venerable designer completing his assignment and retiring to Germany in late 1967. The Indian test pilots were entirely satisfied by the willingness of the German designers to appreciate and endeavour to incorporate the practical suggestions made during the flight testing. Dr. Tank earned admiration and universal praise in Bangalore, not the least for his farsighted genius which was apparent in the potential of the HF-24 design. The HF-24 was planned so as to offer scope for the introduction of some five successive generations of power plants. However, the aircraft had to continue with the Orpheus 703, its very first and interim engine type. Another pay-off from his foresight was the practical feature of a "quick-change" space behind the pilot's seat, which was designed, and utilised, for extra fuel tanks, special avionics, the internal rocket pack or a second seat.

Marut Trainers

Development of the Mark IT trainer and other versions of the HF-24, became the responsibility of an all-Indian team under S.C. Das after 1967. The prototype Marut Mk. IT tandem seating operational trainer (BD-888) was the forty-sixth airframe and, piloted by the then Chief Test Pilot, Wing Commander R.D. Sahni, made its first flight on April 30, 1970. Retaining all features and dimensions of the Mark I, the trainer version differed only in the removal of the internally-housed Matra rocket pack in which place the rear seat was installed. The minimal difference between the fighter and its trainer derivative meant a reduction in development costs and ease of spares interchangeability. Performance ratings were identical with the Mark I, but the Mk. IT had dual controls and a wide selection of systems which enabled the aircraft to be used for several advanced roles, including instrument and armament training. The second Mk. IT followed in March 1971 and these two aircraft completed over 300 test flights before the type was cleared for operational service.

The earlier chapters would bear out the fact that any judgement of the HF-24's progress must be located in the mid-1950s, when conditions for the design and production of supersonic combat aircraft in India were relatively primitive. An extensive range of test, research and development equipment was necessary to prove the quality and reliability of end products but the Indian aircraft industry did not then have even the minimal set-up and virtually no sub-contracting facilities were available. HAL had to do all its own tooling design and fabrication and even basic ground equipment, down to ladders and tractor towing-arms, was necessarily manufactured within. Large capital investments were just not available and the available finances were doled out to five near-simultaneous projects — manufacture of Gnats, Krishaks, Alouette, HT-2 and HJT-16s, besides the HF-24s. The limited budget provided for only two HF-24 prototypes, and a ground test specimen, and the frustrating experience of not finding an answer to the power plant problem had a side repercussion in funds being reallocated to other aircraft projects with fewer technical handicaps. The Indian Air Force did not order the Mark I for some time and induction of aircraft and formation of operational units was pedal-pushed as the Service and HAL kept hopes alive of finding a solution to the power plant problem.

Notwithstanding the best will in the world, albeit an ambitious effort to span the technological gap, the scant resources of finance and trained manpower made it difficult to adhere to schedules of planning and production which were, in retrospect, certainly ambitious. The HF-24 project should be viewed as the foundation upon which HAL was gearing itself for the future. Invaluable experience was accrued and HAL much the 'richer' for it. The Indian engineer and workman had proved his inherent qualities of skill and improvisation.

Further Development Efforts

The high powered Aeronautics Committee headed by C. Subramaniam, the former Minister for Agriculture, formed by the Government of India in December 1967 to examine the country's future defence and civil aircraft requirements, recommended in May 1969 that the HF-24 Mk.I and 1R (or Mk.II) should replace the Hunter and Mystere aircraft in the ground attack role, while development of the Mark III as an interceptor/air superiority fighter should be considered as essential priority. The search for a suitable engine for the Mark III was wide ranging. The R.B.153 two-shaft turbofan was briefly considered with Rolls Royce/Motoren and Turbinen Union (MTU) putting forth a development proposal but HAL was not able to accept the terms of the contract nor, at the time, ready to consider the major redesign of the fuselage and possible unacceptable form drag which adoption of the R.B.153 would have entailed. At one stage, HAL also considered the possibility of employing the French SNECMA Atar 09K-53 single-shaft augmented turbojet of 15,875 Ib. thrust with reheat and, as logical follow-up, the M.53 'Super' Atar, with the superior performance rating of about 19,500 Ib.s.t. Reconfiguration of the Marut to accept a single engine would, however, have been a major task. HAL planning, thus, envisaged the employment of two RB.199 turbofans (the

Tornado's power plant) in a somewhat redesigned Marut airframe. MBB of Germany's participation in the development of this new aircraft was seriously considered and planners at HAL visualised that it have would taken an estimated 4-5 years to develop and adapt the Marut to this series of superior engines. The effort was considered well justified as it would finally have taken the HF-24 to its correct design/performance envelope, cost the Indian government no more than a fourth, about Rs.100 crore in development terms, of what would be needed to finance a new project and utilised a great amount of design and development experience; and avionics and weapon systems would have been simultaneously updated.

HF-73 Strike Aircraft

It was hoped that the HF-24 Marut Mk.III or the HF-73 as the project came to be known, would be available for squadron service by 1981-82 and so provide the IAF its deep penetration strike aircraft from the Eighties. Initially known as the HF-24 Mk. Ill, the aircraft was formally designated the HSS-73 (for "Supersonic Strike"), the number 73 indicating the year in which the firm proposal was submitted. This designation was subsequently changed to HF-73. It was estimated that development time, to the flight of the first prototype, would have been four to five years. Six prototypes and a ground test model of the HF-73 were planned, with squadron entry by 1980-81. It was proposed by MBB to assign a design team to HAL to carry through the project well beyond the definition stage, with the Germans also reportedly keen to secure export rights of the definitive HF-73. The effort was considered well justified as it would have finally enabled the HF-24 to achieve its optimum design/performance envelope, cost the Indian government no more than a quarter of what would be needed to finance an entirely new project, and eventually result in a great amount of contemporary design experience in matters of airframe, engines, avionics and weapon systems. Pursuit of the HF-73 project, when developed by 1980-81, should have made the need for import of Jaguar and MiG-23BN/27 aircraft redundant.

Even while the Government of India was examining the HF-73 proposal and deliberating on the costs involved, HAL continued to request detailed R.B.199-34R data. Despite vigorous efforts made by both MBB and HAL, owing to the R.B.199's non-availability early in 1975, the HF-73 project was reluctantly wound up soon thereafter. Greatly disappointing as this turn of events was, HAL's design and development team did not lose heart, and continued studies with alternate power plants. Although at one stage HAL had also considered the possibility of employing the SNECMA Atar 09K-53 turbojet, reconfiguration of the Marut, to accept a single engine was then considered a major task and was not proceeded with. At a stage, however, when engines of the right dimension and power were not available for political, technical or economic reasons, HAL looked seriously at other possibilities, and with the SNECMA M.53 turbofan in mind, redesign work on the HF-24 for single-engine configuration was carried out in 1975. The French were willing to provide the M.53 on a commercial basis and even while the M.53's future hung in the balance, HAL completed preliminary designs and went ahead with the fabrication of a full scale wooden mock-up.

Rarely has an aircraft of high performance been designed and developed, even in the most industrially advanced countries, where cost and time for development have not been uncertain at best and exceeded substantively in most cases. The issue is that of taking the necessary risks based on empirical studies and a dedicated commitment to the aircraft programme. It was unfortunate that while the HF-24 received adequate governmental support during Nehru's time, this progressively started to be diluted in the following years. Nevertheless the intrepid men at Bangalore led by the redoubtable S.C. Das continued the study of a single-engine HF-24 married to the R-25 (Soviet) engine then being planned for production by HAL at Koraput for the MiG-21bis, and was appropriately known as the HF-25. But this project proposal, too, was overtaken by events with decisions beyond HAL's control, in all probability by the fascination of the Jaguar deal in the works, and did not progress beyond the drawing board. Thus, HAL's HF-24 Marut saga came to a close.

Production of HF-24 Mk.I fighters had meanwhile continued until this model was phased-out in late 1974, with the completion of a second-series order for the aircraft but HAL thereafter delivered the tandem-seat HF-24 Mk.IT operational conversion trainers, and the IAF formed three Marut ground attack squadrons in its Order-of-Battle (ORBAT). The Marut was not an air superiority weapon and was in its element flying at low level in offensive operations during the Indo-Pakistan War of 1971 where it acquitted itself very well. Its pilots had great confidence in the aircraft; and as it was, not a single Marut was lost to, or damaged by, the Pakistan Air Force (PAF) aircraft throughout the two weeks of fighting. A decade after we had been flying the Jaguar in the Air Force, I asked one of our outstanding test pilots how he would rate the Marut with a Rolls Royce engine and the DARIN weapons aiming and attack system (integrated by the IAF on its Jaguars). His answer was prompt and categorical: the Marut would be far superior to the Jaguar!

The HF-24 continued in operational service with the IAF till the early Eighties when the three squadrons concerned were reequipped with the swing-wing MiG-23BN imported from the Soviet Union in 1980-81, most of the Maruts being then relegated to the aircraft 'graveyard' at Chakeri (Kanpur) in 1983-84 although a dozen were flown for another decade by the AD Flight at Bakshi-ka-Talab, near Lucknow, for training with radar operators at the Air Defence School there. This was tragic since at least 40 aircraft out of the 140 being 'retired' had flown less than 20 hours each since manufacture!

The Marut was conceived as a multi-role combat aircraft. Many people have claimed that the effort to design and develop this aircraft was a failure. But that is only half-true. Even though it was somewhat underpowered, once it accelerated, it was an outstanding strike aircraft of its days, which still had an enormous potential for further improvements. There are some little known facts that are relevant to making the final assessment of the HF-24 Marut. One is that the Marut *accident rate was one-eighth* of the most celebrated fighter of the IAF: the Gnat.[24] This means that for every one Marut lost in peace-time training accidents, we were losing eight Gnat aircraft in spite of the fact that pilots posted to Gnat units were required to have more than 300 hours on fighter aircraft and had to be rated on the higher side of average flyers. This was a critical factor if long-term planning of operational readiness and flight safety was to be given any importance. It must also be remembered that the Marut was one of the few heavily armed fighters in the IAF inventory at that time, next – just next – only to the Mystere IVA which came to be known as the "tank-buster;" and, hence, crucial for offensive strike operations. But the dominant philosophy in the Air Force was more in favour of air-to-air warfare, although limited to seeking (local) favourable air situation.

In terms of the plans for the Marut by the top IAF leadership, one personal experience deserves note. In early 1969, I was an Assistant Director in the Training Directorate at Air HQ, and had been arguing with my Director, Air Commodore Marathe about the most suitable replacement for the Vampire, due to retire in a couple of years by 1972. He finally told me to see the Vice Chief of the Air Staff (VCAS), Air Marshal Shivdev Singh and argue my case to him. Initially, I was obviously nervous, as a young squadron leader would be, trying to argue with the VCAS! But he was very kind and willing to listen and discuss. He put me at ease early on, and listened to my thesis with great attention, which was that since we were obviously going in for Soviet MiGs and Sukhois in large numbers and the former was being manufactured in HAL under licence, the logical thing for us in the Air Force to do was to go in for the MiG-15 trainer along with the MiG-17 fighter as the Vampire replacement. He listened for a long time to all my arguments with great patience and asked searching questions. I had flown the MiG-15 trainer and the MiG-17 fighter on instructional duties as the lead-in fighter trainer for nearly a hundred hours in the Iraqi Air Force Academy (near Basra) where I had been sent as a young Flight Lieutenant a couple of years earlier. Having recently flown the MiG-21, I had realised the tremendous advantage of adopting this path, especially since the cockpit layout and emergencies were identical among all these types – an extremely wise concept in Soviet aircraft design philosophy. When I thought I had almost convinced him, he turned and pulled out a file from his cabinet, almost waving it toward me and said that it was too late to do what I wished for since the government had already approved the HF-24 as the Vampire replacement and, hence, the large number of trainers and single-seat fighters already manufactured!

Unfortunately, we never did implement this plan, and the Air Force remained without a lead-in fighter trainer since 1972 till the British Hawk was purchased more than three decades later under the rubric of AJT (Advanced Jet Trainer) although the La Fontaine Committee had strongly recommended in 1982 that we acquire/build an AJT as early as possible while employing the MiG-21 as the trainer at this stage.[25] The main objection was that the HF-24 was too underpowered to be able to operate from Hakimpet (over 2,000 ft altitude) and the runway could not be extended. But efforts to argue that the OTU (Operational Training Unit) could be based at a training base at around sea level did not enthuse most of my seniors. Perhaps the problem was that HAL had not been able to find solutions to the frequent snags that reduced serviceability and added to field maintenance workload, especially when spare parts were not easily available. However, the Pakistan Air Force kept using the MiG-15/MiG17 combination for fighter conversion for decades till recently.

LICENSED PRODUCTION

The First Jet Fighter: Vampire

As noted earlier, the first aircraft produced by HAL under licence (not counting those of the pre-war years) was the Percival Prentice trainer. But the first jet fighter to be produced under licence in India was the de Havilland Vampire. The aircraft had entered service somewhat late to take part in World War II. The first Vampire (actually three of them) was flown to New Delhi for demonstration on November 4, 1948. With a speed of 500 mph and high manoeuvrability, it was quite an aircraft in operations. The Vampire was armed with four 20 mm Hispano cannons in the nose and could carry eight 3" rockets or 1,000 lb of bombs under each wing. The initial models were soon superseded by improved versions, with more powerful engines and the EMk.3 also had increased internal fuel capacity. Three such models were diverted to the RIAF from RAF stocks to facilitate trials in tropical conditions and prepare for large-scale induction of the jet fighter into Indian service. The export version of the Vampire Mk.5 was designated the FB Mk. 52 and could carry 2,000 lb of bombs or rockets under the wings besides external fuel tanks. The Vampire FB52, which supplanted all piston-engine fighters of the Indian Air Force, was powered by a de Havilland Goblin 2 centrifugal- flow turbojet rated at 3,100 lb thrust.

The Government of India entered into a licence agreement with the de Havilland Company of Hatfield in England in March 1950 which covered the eventual manufacture of a large number of Vampire FB52s, of which the first few were put together from imported major assemblies. The first HAL-built Vampire flew on February 21, 1952, and a number of piston-engine fighter squadrons were then reequipped with the type. The Vampire T.55 (export model T.ll) was also selected with a few imported and the rest built by HAL, including some assembled from imported material, the last HAL-built Vampire being handed over to the Indian Air Force in December 1960. In the late Fifties, HAL undertook the modification of a number of Vampire T.55s to the photo- reconnaissance configuration which operated for nearly two decades with No. 101 FR Squadron.

The first fighter squadron equipped with Vampire FB Mk52, No. 7 Squadron, which had been equipped with the Tempest fighter-bombers and served with great distinction in the 1947-48 War, became operational in 1949. More than 400

Vampire single-seat fighters were procured, almost all of them assembled or progressively manufactured at HAL.[26] In addition, 60 Vampire T-11/55 were also produced (with 10 assembled from CKD and 50 manufactured) at HAL. The Vampire NF Mk.54 with No. 10 Squadron became operational as the first night fighter squadron and was based at Safdarjung (and later Palam) airfield in New Delhi during May 1952. Vampires began to be used for fighter conversion at the OTU at Hakimpet from 1954 onwards. When seven Auxiliary Air Force squadrons were raised in 1955-57, the first two raised in 1955 (No. 51 Squadron in New Delhi and No. 52 Squadron in Bombay) were equipped with Vampire aircraft by 1957, while the others remained mostly with HT-2 aircraft. All seven squadrons were incorporated into the regular Air Force in 1962 in view of the rising tensions and war with China in late 1962. Vampires were used in the Indo-Pakistan Wars of 1965 and 1971 where they performed with great credit. The Vampire aircraft was finally retired in 1973 without a proper replacement.

The "Sabre-Killer" Gnat

The Air Force's interest in an air superiority fighter had evolved from the days of the Spitfire and the urge after independence to build a "balanced" air force which would have all capabilities, except that the issue of a long-range bomber remained ambivalent. The IAF had entered the jet age with the Vampire and after the articulated threats from Pakistan in early 1951 and military mobilisation for a potential war, and the consequent programme for expansion, it was but natural that many more and modern fighters would be procured. During the 1951 crisis, it was found that key parts in the guns of the Vampire fleet had not been supplied by the manufacturer. Hence, the need to acquire a fighter from a different source was accepted and three squadrons worth of Dassault Ouragon (Toofani in India) were acquired in 1953. The crisis also led to the government approving the expansion of the IAF from 10 to 15 squadrons. Inevitably, the search for additional aircraft continued.

An Indian Air Force team was in the UK engaged in evaluating the Supermarine Swift being considered as a contender for the new IAF fighter requirement. The Swift was not found suitable. Meanwhile, the precursor of the Gnat, the Midge, being developed by Folland, under the design leadership of William Edward Petter, for the light fighter contest for a NATO requirement (the other contestant was the Italian G-90) had flown for the first time on August 11, 1954. Its developed version was to be known as the Gnat. The IAF team transferred its interest to the projected Gnat as a result of the impressive displays given by the Midge. The leader of the IAF team, Air Commodore P.C. Lal (later MD of HAL and Air Chief Marshal and Chief of the Air Staff), became the first foreign pilot to fly the Midge in mid-November 1954, being followed by then Group Captain (later Air Chief Marshal) H. Moolgavkar and Wing Commander Roshan Suri.

Although the Indian pilots universally recommended that the Gnat be considered for the IAF, negotiations were initially somewhat protracted as Petter was reluctant to agree to his creation wearing anything but RAF roundels. However, Petter soon overcame his reluctance and gave his full attention to the development of the Gnat for India and, in fact, offered his services to the Indian government and *proposed the establishment of a design bureau in India for the development of more advanced versions of the Gnat.*[27] However, by September 1956, when the Indian government concluded the licensed manufacturing agreement with Folland, Dr. Kurt Tank was already in India and engaged in developing the HF-24. It is generally believed that South Block turned down the Petter proposal because the HF-24 design and development was already approved and the Indian government could not then afford the luxury of two simultaneous jet fighter development programmes. But the reality also must be noted that at that time, the government accepted the necessity of expansion of the Air Force and had contracted for the Mystere IVA. In addition, the decision to acquire the Hunter aircraft was made a whole year later and it would take a couple of years for the aircraft to be delivered. The Gnat was already flying though full development would still take a couple of years. The more logical approach ought to have been to go in straight for the improved Gnat version that Petter had offered. It may be argued that in view of the international situation which had necessitated the expansion of the Air Force, there was some urgency to get the Gnat. But nearly 115 Mystere IV fighter-bombers had been acquired and delivered by 1957 and while three squadrons were equipped with them, more than adequate numbers of Mysteres had been kept in reserve and could have been used to raise three more squadrons any time (which, in fact, was done after the Sino-Indian War of 1962). But in 1956, the Sino-Indian friction was at a low level and even the northern borders were being manned by the Indian police under the overall management of the IB (Intelligence Bureau). It appears that the long-term gains of Petter's proposal were not given the serious consideration that they deserved unless the reason was that, in the beginning, only four squadrons of Gnats (64 aircraft) were expected to be raised and the cost and effort of another design bureau were considered superfluous for this requirement.

The official history claims that the Gnat as eventually produced was to cost only a third as much as other fighters of comparable performance in capital outlay and operating expenditure per flying hour, and because of the radical economics and relative simplicity, the light fighter philosophy closely identified with Indian requirements. One assumes that the "advanced" version of the Gnat would still have been a light fighter and, hence, not drastically different in terms of costs, etc. Thus, another opportunity to build an appropriate aircraft industry (with design and development capacity set by an experienced British group) was allowed to go by without any apparently sound reasons beyond the understanding in the South Block and HAL, especially since only four squadrons of Gnats were originally visualised. The cost of Petter's proposal to set up another design bureau should have been compared with the cost of not accepting it. Not accepting Petter's proposal was perhaps the first step in limiting our self-reliance by limiting our design and development capabilities which in the early days could have been set only with external assistance.

By 1955, Bristol had produced the initial Orpheus engine then rated at 4,000 lb s.t. (1.814 kg) thrust, and the result of its installation in Petter's airframe was to be seen in an "astonishing display of speed and manoeuvrability" that marked the public debut of the Gnat at Farnborough in September 1955. On September 15, 1956, the Government of India concluded an agreement with Folland for production of the Gnat under licence at Bangalore, the agreement covering an initial supply of complete Gnat Mk.Is and further sets of components for progressive assembly by HAL. Meanwhile, flight testing of the Gnat continued at Chilbolten and nearly five hundred flying hours were completed. Wing Commander Suranjan Das was nominated from the IAF to Chilbolten and attached to the Gnat Flight Development team. Late in 1957, the sixth Gnat was transported to India in an IAF Fairchild C-119G Packet. This first Indian Gnat, sporting the IAF

serial IE 1059 was to be used as a development aircraft. The Aircraft
and Armament Testing Unit (A&ATU), IAF, at Kanpur, formed
the Gnat Handling Flight in the spring of 1958, with four Folland-
built Gnats and six IAF officers. The complete test programme at
Chilbolten and Kanpur had resulted in a final development Gnat
which had all the modifications incorporated—from the adoption
of power operated inboard ailerons, modification of the tail to a
fully powered slab, to final cockpit plan and incorporation of gun
blast reducers. But, for the very first time, the IAF had to work
out its own Standard Operating Procedures (SOPs) for an aircraft
without relying on a foreign operator's experience, establish
syllabi for training and evolve maintenance techniques.

The Gnat at this stage was still very "raw" and had to be
moulded by the IAF into a fully proven service aircraft. The
major problem encountered involved the flying control system.
For horizontal tail control, the Hobson design consisted of
hydraulic motor driving twin screw jacks which rotated the
all-flying tailplane through an epicyclical reduction gear. The
Hobson system was initially unable to take the loads required
under service conditions for any restriction in the flow of
hydraulic fluid would result in back pressure and low hydraulic
power output with the motor not generating the required force
to operate the tailplane. Excessive friction in the screw jacks
needed to be eliminated and the quantum of maintenance
checks had to be increased to far beyond the manufacture's
recommendation. The Gnat Handling Flight was to go
through a somewhat trying period in coming to terms with the
light fighter and, as at Chilbolten, fatalities were suffered as
the ingenious, yet unconventional, systems were harnessed. By
mid-1959, it was decided to form the first Gnat operational
unit, this receiving the first batch of Folland-build Gnat Mk. Is
on March 18, 1960, at Ambala.

Meanwhile, at Bangalore, HAL was preparing for the manufacture of the Gnat and a batch of engineers and assembly superintendents was deputed to Folland for attachment in late 1958. Some new factory buildings for the project were completed in 1959 but with the last Vampire F.B. 52 delivered to the IAF in December 1960, Gnat production lines were planned in the former Vampire assembly hangars. Two hangars were allocated for structure with a third for assembly and final erection. A batch of Gnats, received in "fly-away" major assembly form, were assembled in 1959, initially under the general supervision of Folland representatives. The first HAL built Gnat was one of many assembled from the CKD form and delivered on November 18, 1959, but it was not till 1962 that the first Gnat, produced from raw materials, flew on May 21, 1962, six years after the agreement to manufacture them in India had been signed. A number of modifications had been carried out in between, the most basic being a change in the radio compass and the provision of an additional 25 gallons in internal fuel in saddle tanks aft of the fuselage break joint.

A fourth Gnat unit was in the process of formation when tension on the borders erupted into full-scale hostilities in September 1965. In that month, HAL rose to the occasion and working round the clock through the three weeks of the shooting war, sixteen Gnats were completed. Test flying by day, butt-testing at night, HAL delivered two Gnats to the IAF *each day* from September 15 to 22, 1965. The four squadrons of Gnats provided commendable service during the India-Pakistan War initiated by Pakistan on September 1, 1965. Its high manoeuvrability, and small size made it difficult for enemy aircraft to spot it early and above all, the skill of the pilots, gave it a clear edge over the technologically superior F-86s and F-104s of the Pakistan Air Force. The results of air combat would have been somewhat more in the Gnat's favour if its guns had not been jamming on critical occasions during air combat. After the first F-86 had been shot down by a Gnat in air combat on September 3, the Pakistan Air Force started to shift its operational posture toward a greater defensive deployment. The Gnat acquired the nick-name of "Sabre Killer" across the country, with the media particularly extolling, though not really true, its virtues as a home-made fighter superior to the best of America's given to Pakistan. As a result, the aircraft scheduled to stop production in 1966 after the fourth squadron had been raised, was to continue to be produced to equip eight squadrons although its basic technical problems had not been solved.

After the war, the sporadic failure of the longitudinal control system received priority attention and intense research and trials resulted in more modifications incorporated, mostly in an effort to reduce screw jack friction. By 1968, the improvements were firmed and all Gnats retrofitted accordingly. The new squadrons achieved operational status rapidly. HAL briefly studied the possibilities of "navalising" the Gnat for the aircraft carrier INS *Vikrant*. Folland had themselves once proposed a Gnat with extensive high lift devices on both leading and trailing edges of the wings for possible carrier operation but the tasks of strengthening the Gnat's undercarriage within weight restrictions made the proposal impractical. Besides, its limited range and endurance made it unsuitable for the Indian Navy.

Pakistan, which had been going toward increasing domestic instability because of ethnic chauvinism of the Punjabi-Pathan military-bureaucratic combine, discriminating against Bengalis and other ethnic communities, erupted into a military crackdown in East Pakistan, described by the foreign media

as a genocide starting at the end of March 1971 after the
Pakistan government headed by General Yahya Khan refused to
implement the results of Pakistan's only general election (when
the Bengali political party had won a clear majority in Pakistan's
Parliament). The continuing repression of the Bengalis led
to over 10 million refugees streaming into India. There was
a clear risk, and evidence, of the Pakistan Army initiating an
aggression from East Pakistan as early as April 1971. General
Niazi, the Pakistan Army C-in-C of its Eastern Command
believed that "Indian Army was not prepared to face a sudden
onslaught from an unexpected direction." [28] The situation had
kept deteriorating till on November 23, the PAF intrusion into
West Bengal with four F-86s was intercepted by IAF Gnats that
shot down three Sabres. A full-fledged war started after Pakistan
carried out a surprise attack on Indian airfields on December 3,
1971. The Gnats performed extremely well. A detachment of
Gnats was stationed at Srinagar which was often attacked by the
PAF because reaction time to intercept the frequent attacks was
extremely short because of the hills around the valley. One of the
greatest advantages of the Gnat was that it could be scrambled
and airborne in less than 38 seconds! On December 14, the
PAF attacked Srinagar with six F-86s. Flying Officer Nirmaljit
Singh Sekhon was on ORP and got airborne while the Sabres
were strafing the airfield. During the ensuing low level combat,
Sekhon hit two Sabres before he was shot down. He was awarded
India's highest gallantry award, the Param Vir Chakra — the first
and so far the only one, in the best traditions of the Indian Air
Force. Thus, the Gnat earned a unique distinction in the history
of India, besides Sekhon who flew it in the face of heavy odds,
no doubt knowing the end result.

The last Gnat Mk. I was delivered to the Indian Air Force
on January 31, 1974, but HAL had been heavily engaged for

some years with the major overhaul of Gnats. The light fighter's structure was simple and rugged and designed for a minimum fatigue life of 5,000 hours. HAL had had nearly 15 years experience with the production of the Gnat and it was planned to utilise the same facilities, jigs and tools for the proposed Gnat Mk. II, christened Ajeet, in November 1973. The Mk. II, as being developed at Bangalore, was a HAL effort conforming to an IAF specification and (inexplicably) no assistance has sought from the British company, nor did the Ajeet have any connection with the original Gnat Mk. II proposed by Folland in 1956.

Early in 1972, a committee was formed under the chairmanship of Air Commodore (later Air Vice Marshal) J.J. Bouche of the Indian Air Force, comprising members from the air arm, Hindustan Aeronautics and the Scientific Adviser's office. The problems of the Gnat were reviewed in depth by this committee and urgent solutions worked on. In May 1972, close on the heels of the committee finalising its recommendations in March 1972, a draft Air Staff Requirement for an "improved" Gnat was issued by Air HQ, referring to the Bouche Committee recommendations and emphasising aspects of operational and maintenance nature.

The Gnat situation was examined by two other technical bodies at about the same time, but more from the point of scientific enquiry. The Bhabha Atomic Research Centre Scientists Panel as well as the Bangalore Scientists Panel (from the Indian Institute of Science, Aeronautical Development Establishment and National Aeronautical Laboratory) went into various aspects of the Gnat and their recommendations on product-improvement and updating were broadly in line with those of the Bouche Committee. Basically, improvements were sought in the system for longitudinal control and design of the hydraulic system. Installation of a new ejection seat, brakes and wheels was suggested, as also the incorporation of contemporary avionics, provision of additional fuel in the integral wing tanks and improved gun feed arrangements. In the original thinking, it was proposed that the IAF would return its Gnats to HAL in a phased programme for retrofitting of these various improvements, the modified aircraft being referred to as the Mk.IA. In fact, some Mk.Is were fitted with updated systems and returned to the Service.

However, with the transformation of the role to ground attack and in view of the Air HQ proposal to order 80 additional aircraft, HAL began to view this as a completely new, major project and the aircraft was given the Gnat Mk.II designation; the government decision was taken rather hurriedly and the formal "go-ahead" for the project was given in June 1972. As the aircraft went through its transformation, it was rechristened Ajeet ("Invincible") in November 1973, and the final Air Staff Requirement was frozen in June 1974. The new aircraft was visualised as a battlefield air superiority fighter and ground attack aircraft.

With well over a decade of Gnat production experience behind it, HAL was confident of bringing about these major improvements in the aircraft without elaborate redesigning and did not find it necessary to approach the British company for assistance: the philosophy could be summed up as "seeking maximum possible overall improvements at minimum cost and in the shortest time scale". In all, some 50 modifications were introduced and the degree of commonality between the Gnat Mk. I and Mk. II reduced to less than 60 percent. "Wetting" the wings was a major exercise but was carried out smoothly as HAL had some years of experience in the development and manufacture of the HF-24 Marut's wing, which already incorporated integral fuel tanks. Notwithstanding these, the fuel leaks from the integral wing fuel tanks remained a persistent problem till the HF-24 and Ajeet were phased out. The four underwing stations were no doubt freed for the carriage of a variety of armament stores. The inboard hard points could carry 500-lb (227-kg) bombs, "Arrow" Type 122 rocket pods (19 x 68-mm rockets apiece), or practice stores, while the outboard points would carry the rocket pods or 30-Imp Gal (136-1) drop tanks, specially developed by HAL for the Ajeet. The Ajeet retained the twin 30-mm Aden Mk. 4 cannon, but with some modifications in the gun feed system, as also the Vinten type G-90 gun-camera. The Gnat's earlier gunsight was replaced by the Ferranti Isis F-195 gunsight, this equipment also made at HAL's Lucknow Division.

The system for longitudinal control needed much improvement and HAL was in constant dialogue with Lucas over the Hobson unit which had been the cause of so much anxiety and accidents in the early days. A new Hobson unit was evolved by Lucas at the suggestion of HAL. Indicative of the high standards that were set and enforced, HAL rejected a considerable number of the initial batches of this new unit. In the autumn of 1972, HAL's Design Bureau incorporated some of the new systems in a standard Gnat Mk. I and this aircraft was used in the proving of the modified hydraulics and new flying controls. A second Gnat was made available to the Design Bureau directly from the shop floor, which became the development flying vehicle for test-proving the new avionics and individual systems, first flying in mid-1973. By this time, the Gnat Mk. I production programme was fast drawing to a close, with the last example of the light fighter delivered to the IAF in January 1974. The last two of the final Gnats on order were, in fact, not completed but were earmarked as prototypes of the proposed Mk. II or Ajeet, whilst one other airframe was completed for static testing.

The last Gnat manufactured by HAL, thus, became the first Ajeet prototype, incorporating virtually all the major changes and modifications, its maiden flight taking place on March 6, 1975. The second prototype followed into the air on November 5, 1975 and these two aircraft made over 300 development flights to prove the systems and aerodynamics. Flutter testing was completed successfully and no major problems encountered. In all phases of the flight test programme, HAL test pilots and the Design Bureau coordinated efforts with the Air Force's Aircraft & System Testing Establishment (ASTE), also located at Bangalore airport.

A large production run of Ajeets to equip eight fighter squadrons was originally programmed and it was also planned that with the availability of sufficient Ajeets to form new squadrons, the Gnats would be returned to Bangalore for extensive modifications, bringing them up to full Ajeet standards. The order was subsequently reduced in 1979, and these formed the equipment of four IAF squadrons, the last Ajeets being delivered in 1982. A requiem for the Gnat/Ajeet is in order.

A major empirical study of IAF fighter aircraft loss rates was undertaken in late 1977 to study in greater detail the accident rates in each fleet of aircraft rather than the unit/command-wise approach that had been followed for decades. Data on accidents was available in Air HQ going back to 1949. The study revealed surprising results and was, therefore, validated at the IAF's EDP (Electronic Data Processing) Centre in Delhi Cantonment. One of the results was that the accident rate of the HF-24 Marut was approximately one-eighth that of the Gnat/Ajeet. With little or no signs of any dramatic breakthrough in Gnat/Ajeet flight safety records, it was obvious that the aircraft more suited purely from the flight safety point of view was the HF-24 Marut designed in HAL (unlike the Gnat) and totally developed in HAL (again unlike the Gnat whose development was substantively undertaken at the Folland factory by British and Indian test pilots). Since the Ajeet was to be used primarily for ground attack (mostly battlefield support of the Army), comparison on operational parameters also showed that the HF-24 Marut was superior in various aspects (like combat radius of action, weapons payload, etc.) by at least 30-40 percent compared to the Ajeet. This study was to finally lead to serious rethinking about the fundamental design weakness of the Ajeet and the plan for 8 squadrons was shelved and the programme restricted to what had already been manufactured and then retired early.

OUTRIGHT PURCHASE AND IMPORT

In early 1951, the Pakistani Prime Minister Liaquat Ali Khan, under pressure from his army, threatened India with a war (on Kashmir). Prime Minister Nehru ordered a military mobilisation in response to Pakistani moves. During the mobilisation, it was discovered that the Vampire (the main frontline fighter at that time) had some parts from its guns missing probably because they were not supplied by the manufacturer. This led to the policy of diversifying the sources of weapons and equipment not designed and developed indigenously. This, in turn, began the search for a non-British combat aircraft. Such weapons were not available to India from the United States; and, hence, the main source became France. The Marcel Dassault Ouragon (named Toofani in India) was selected for the IAF in 1953.[29]

By the mid-1950s, Pakistan had joined the US-led military alliance ostensibly against the Communist countries (Soviet Union and China being military allies). The Indian Air Force sought expansion from the sanctioned 15-squadron to the 25-squadron level.[30] This, in turn, led to the acquisition of Mystere IVA from France and Hunter fighters from Britain while the design and development of the HF-24 was also started. Soon after, in order to obtain adequate numbers of aircraft, with the Vampire already getting old for frontline service, New Delhi ordered Hunter 56 fighter-bombers from the UK. Three squadrons with Canberra light bomber and interdictor aircraft purchased from English Electric Company in the UK were also raised besides one for strategic reconnaissance.

One of the rare supplies of aircraft by the United States to India was the sale of the Fairchild Packet C-119G medium transport aircraft (the other being a few Sikorsky S-55 helicopters). The Packet was a good aircraft, including for air dropping men and supplies from its rear door. But the IAF soon realised that it had severe limitations in operating at high altitudes in the Himalayas; and this is exactly where the need for air-dropped supplies was the greatest after the northern frontier became live after 1959. The solution to the problem was finally found by the IAF with its own resources in cooperation with HAL (the agency which overhauled the aircraft).

Our Air Attache in Washington DC in 1960 was then Group Captain (later to become the Chief of the Air Staff in 1978) Idris Latif. He came across an aviation magazine which described an ex-USAF Fairchild C-82 cargo aircraft fitted with a Westinghouse J-30 jet pack on top of its fuselage for operations from high altitude airfields in Central and South America. Always looking for ways and means of enhancing IAF capabilities, Latif contacted Steward Davis Inc. in California, the company that had carried out the modification on PanAm aircraft. The company came up with the solution to mount a Westinghouse J-3400 jet engine to provide thrust of nearly 1,600 kg. Group Captain Latif sent in his recommendation to Air HQ and it eventually resulted in the fitment of J-34 jet pack on top of the fuselage of the Packet. Later, it was found that at the higher reaches of the Himalayas and the airfields like Daulat Beg Oldi, the payload had to be reduced substantively for safe operations. It was then decided to install the Orpheus 701 as the replacement jet pack for greater thrust. And the Packet with the Orpheus jet pack was finally landed at Daulat Beg Oldi, over 17,000 ft above sea level, the highest airfield in the world. Incidentally, the jet pack was run on Packet's 115-octane fuel in lieu of the ATF (Aviation Turbine Fuel) normally used in jet engines.

Two squadrons each of two types of light transport – the DHC Caribou and DHC Otter – purchased directly from Canada, rendered yeomen service during the Sino-Indian War in 1962. In fact, one Otter squadron airlifted a whole brigade in two days laterally across the mountains to provide reinforcements.

Notes

1. Major General B.D. Kapur, head of defence R&D as the CCR&D till 1958, in his book *Building a Defence Technology Base* (New Delhi: Lancer International, 1990), p. 63. Emphasis in original.

2. For a seminal study on India's self-reliance in the aerospace sector, see Ajay Singh, "Quest for Self-Reliance" (Study commissioned by the Rajiv Gandhi Foundation in 1995) published in Jasjit Singh, *India's Defence Spending: Assessing Future Needs* (New Delhi: Knowledge World, 2000 2nd Edition), pp. 125-156.

3. Pushpinder Singh, *Diamonds in the Sky: Sixty Years of HAL 1940-2001* (New

Delhi: Society for Aerospace Studies, 2001), p. 36.

4. Air Marshal M.S. Chaturvedi, *History of the Indian Air Force* (New Delhi: Vikas Publishing House, 1978), p. 69.

5. Air Commodore A.L. Saigal, ed., *Birth of an Air Force: The Memoirs of Air Vice Marshal Harjinder Singh* (New Delhi: Palit & Palit Publishers, 1977), pp. 229-231.

6. The RIAF was sanctioned a 10-squadron force as a back-up to the RAF's 11 squadrons in India. At the time of independence, the RAF squadrons left India and the RIAF's 10 squadron were divided between Pakistan and India, leaving the latter with 6 squadrons of fighter aircraft and half a squadron of transport aircraft. The first priority, therefore, was to build the Air Force back to a 10-squadron force and then expand it to 25 squadrons as per pre-partition plans.

7. A. Martin Wainwright, *Inheritance of Empire: Britain, India, and the Balance of Power in Asia, 1938-55* (Westport: Praeger Publishers, 1994), p. 91.

8. Kapur, n. 1, p. 47.

9. Ibid., pp. 5-6.

10. Ibid., p. 17.

11. It would be instructive to compare this report with the Kelkar Committee Report on Ordnance Factories rendered nearly six decades later.

12. Singh, n. 3, p. 38.

13. Ibid., p. 42.

14. Air Chief Marshal L.M. Katre, Chief of the Air Staff in 1984-86, was deputed at that time as a Squadron Leader to set up the Ghana Air Force.

15. Alka Sen, *Glimpses into Indian Aviation History 1910-1997* (Bombay: Indian Aviation News Service Pvt Ltd, 1998), p. 447.

16. Chaturvedi, n. 4, p. 113. See also p. 130.

17. Raju G.C. Thomas, *The Defence of India: A Budgetary Perspective of Strategy and Politics* (Delhi: Macmillan Company of India, 1978), p. 182.

18. Kapur, n. 1, p. 79.

19. Some sources cite the sum as GBP 1 million [see Chris Smith, *India's Ad Hoc Arsenal: Direction or Drift in Defence Policy?* (SIPRI and Oxford University Press, 1994)], p. 161.

20. Ibid., p. 161.

21. Group Captain Jacob Chakko, *Memoirs* (Los Angles: Published by Chakko, 1999), p. 228.

22. See *Estimates Committee, 1967-68*, 12th Report, 4th Lok Sabha, "Defence Research and Development Organisation" Ministry of Defence, Government of India, 1969, pp. 3-6.

23. Smith, n. 19, p. 161.

24. While the Gnat acquired a great reputation in India as the F-86 Sabre Killer in 1965 War, Pakistani official records of its air force losses in air combat show only two Sabres being shot down by the Gnats against four by the Hunters (The number of squadrons of Hunters and Gnats being equal). See P.V.S. Jagan Mohan, *The India-Pakistan War of 1965* (New Delhi: Manohar Publishers, 2005), Appendix C, Table C, pp. 348-349.

25. This report had been approved by Mrs Indira Gandhi as the Defence Minister when she was the PM.

26. Sen, n. 15, p. 350.

27. Singh, n. 3, p. 47.

28. Lieutenant General A.A.K. Niazi, *The Betrayal of East Pakistan* (New Delhi: Manohar Publishers, 1998), p. 65.

29. Chaturvedi, n. 4, p. 104.

30. Ibid., p. 113.

5

Self-Reliance Fractured
Decline of the Design Capacity

It is our finding that licence production inhibits indigenous development; in the present case, it would completely extinguish development.

— Aeronautics Committee,
generally called the C. Subramaniam Committee[1]

The above statement was a crucial conclusion in the history of the Indian aircraft industry. Coming from this high-powered committee, one would have assumed that South Block would have given it due importance. This high-powered committee's report was submitted in 1968 when there was marginal indigenous design and development taking place. The design and development work on the HF-24 multi-role combat aircraft had been completed and the aircraft had been inducted into service. The only project undergoing further development was the HJT-16 Mk.II intermediate trainer which had been designed and developed by Raj Mahindra, then head of the HAL's Design Bureau. The other aircraft to be designed during that period was the HPT-32 piston-engine primary trainer (which ran into serious problems in failing to meet the ASR), till, a little later, the IAF, left without any option, gave a major concession to the ASR and inducted it into service. But these were the last indigenous designs till the Light Combat Aircraft (LCA) three decades later. The conclusions of the Subramaniam Committee proved to be prophetic in those two decades by the end of which most of the designers who took part in the HF-24 design and development had, by and large, retired, and the HAL Design Bureau was left with no real work.

Some people would question the last statement on the basis that HAL had designed the Ajeet starting in the early 1970s. However, this was actually a Gnat with some modifications and initially was even named as Gnat Mk.II. The original plan was to have manufactured Gnat aircraft for equipping only four squadrons. But after the war in 1965 where it performed extremely well, and in view of its low cost and the need to expand the Air Force to its interim force level of 35 combat squadrons, HAL was asked in 1966 to produce additional aircraft to man eight squadrons. The Gnat Mk.II became an apparently logical follow-on programme. Even at that stage, if Mr Petter's offer of designing a somewhat larger Gnat (somewhat like the Gnat trainer in the RAF of the Red Arrows fame, which continued to render yeoman service at a critical level of flying training for a very long time) had been accepted, we might have had a good indigenous designed aircraft. However, the Gnat Mk.II, soon to be renamed Ajeet, turned out to be very disappointing, with innumerable problems (like fuel leaks from the integral wing tanks, etc.) without producing any solutions to the central problem of the Gnat, that is, the flight control system, etc. HAL also designed a Gnat trainer within the airframe of the Gnat aircraft. Unfortunately the solitary prototype crashed and the programme of producing Gnat trainers ended with it.

No wonder, HAL found itself unable to take on the task of design and development of the Advanced Jet Trainer (AJT) identified by the La Fontaine Committee as a critical and urgent requirement in 1982 to fill the vacuum in pilot training at the Stage III level. Nor did HAL attempt to design the LCA which originally was meant to be a much simpler aircraft as a replacement for MiG-21 aircraft by the late 1980s based on redesign of the front fuselage of the MiG-21 to remove the main handicaps (susceptibility to bird strikes, poor cockpit visibility, lack of even a cockpit cooling system leave alone any air-conditioning system). This would also have made it possible to utilise the 450-kg ballast weight widely distributed in that area consequent to miniaturising of various systems and components over the decades for internal fuel, extending the operational range/payload of the aircraft.

Unfortunately, the LCA, with its hyped up specifications, far beyond what the Operations Branch of the Air Force had proposed as a MiG-21 replacement, or for that matter within the available design capabilities of HAL which had been struggling to start design and development through the three decades since the HF-24 design started, was handicapped from the very beginning. And, hence, an ad-hoc organisation was set up in the shape of the ADA (Aeronautical Development Agency) under the Scientific Adviser to the Defence Minister, concurrently also the head of DRDO as well as Secretary Defence (R&D), as a registered society to undertake the design and development of the LCA with foreign consultancies with a number of countries. Inevitably, the LCA became a "prestigious" national project and the best human resources of HAL's various entities were drawn in to undertake it.

The central point that we need to note is that in the post-Nehru era, India acquired a large number of aircraft mostly from the Soviet Union and/or Europe, essentially France (to maintain a level of self-reliance through diversifying the sources of supply) to build up and sustain its force level. But **unfortunately, HAL (the sole aircraft industrial establishment) stopped the fledgling efforts at design and development of**

aircraft. One can argue that the LCA has been designed in the country. But a little over thirty years elapsed since the HF-24 design was commenced before the design of the LCA started to take shape in late 1987. During these three decades, aviation technology has undergone dramatic changes, multiplying the challenges enormously, made more complex by overloading the expected design specifications. Even then, an ad-hoc organisation, the ADA had to be set up for this purpose (since HAL apparently was considered incapable, though almost all the designers and engineers were deputed from different divisions of HAL to ADA). Logically, these could easily have been brought together in the legitimate existing Design Bureau of HAL so that the potential disjunction between design and production did not hamstring the programme later. Even if a new ad-hoc institution like the ADA had to be set up, it should have been organisationally integrated vertically with the Indian Air Force, the real stakeholder in the programme, which would ultimately fly the aircraft and possibly fight a hostile air force, to win. The public impression has been that there was serious infighting among the scientists on some fundamental issues concerning the principle of integrated or ad-hoc arrangements for design and development. If that was so – and Dr. V.S. Valluri's accounts indicate even the differences between the civil bureaucracy and the scientists, creating further disjunctions – this is a sad commentary on a number of institutions, especially South Block which carries the onerous responsibility of national defence.

In fact, the only trainer that HAL designed and developed after the mid-1960s was the replacement for the HT-2 primary trainer, the HPT-32 which unfortunately was grounded in 2009 after a number of fatal accidents due to engine failure and other causes. Although there were signs of its recovery, HAL's design bureau had dissipated by the 1980s. It may be mentioned here that in spite of the urgent need of a suitable lead-in fighter trainer (the advanced jet trainer) as it came to be called in India, HAL was not considered capable of designing such an aircraft and a long search for an imported aircraft started, till a contract for the British Hawk trainer was signed in 2004. The result has been that the three-strand self-reliance model established soon after independence has severely suffered since the key strand – that of indigenous design and development – actually seems to have been given up in preference for the more convenient licensed production. But the problem is that this demands dependence on external sources all the time, while creating a false sense of security and capability.

The Sino-Indian War resulted in immediate sanction of expansion of the IAF from the earlier 33-squadron force (which had yet to reach even the level of the previously sanctioned 25-squadron force). In 1963, the Emergency Committee of the Cabinet actually authorised the expansion of the Air Force to the 64-squadron level to include 14 squadrons of transport aircraft and 50 combat squadrons. The latter included one heavy bomber squadron. Considering the scale of effort and resources required, it was later decided that *as an interim solution,* India should aim for a 45-squadron force (35 combat and 10 transport squadrons) since resources and aircraft were not available! The expansion would naturally demand expanded radar, communications, repair and overhaul facilities, training institutions for pilots, technical and administrative officers and airmen, etc. Since the Chinese had declared only a unilateral ceasefire, the possibility of resumption of hostilities by the Chinese remained and, hence, provided an impetus for urgent expansion in all sectors and facilities. The most critical requirement, of course, was aircraft, pilots and technical personnel. It is in this context that we need to see the aircraft industry in the post-Nehru era.

So far, the best account of the initiation of the LCA design process comes from Dr. S.R. Valluri former Director of NAL (National Aeronautical Laboratory at that time) over a long time and a well known scientist and aeronautical expert. Before going into that, we need to record the development of the after-burner (reheat) for the Bristol Orpheus 703 engine by the then fledgling GTRE (Gas Turbine Research Establishment), a laboratory under the DRDO. Dr. Valluri records that GTRE was able to successfully demonstrate its design performance of 20 percent increase in thrust on the test-bed with the afterburner designed by it.[2] But instead of redesigning the fuselage to accommodate the afterburner to reduce any potential increase in drag to the minimum, S.C. Das, then in charge of the programme, decided to fit the afterburner with a sudden increase in the aft area end of the fuselage. Inevitably, the added drag led to nullifying the extra thrust developed by the indigenously designed reheat system. Instead of following up on the programme, the HF-24 programme was prematurely closed.

The Aeronautics Committee headed by C. Subramaniam had recommended that HAL should take up the development of a combat aircraft, a Short Take-Off and Landing (STOL) aircraft, and a helicopter.[3] After the attempts to convert the Gnat into the Ajeet multi-role combat aircraft (started in 1973) on the existing platform which failed to produce the desired results, it took another two decades after the C. Subramaniam Committee had submitted its report for the combat aircraft design to get under way. The STOL never saw the light of day; and the helicopter design, held in a state of suspension for a long time, finally started to see some action

under the leadership of Raj Mahendra. As noted earlier, the
LCA became the major indigenously designed programme.
However, this was not left to HAL, the only and ultimate
manufacturer of the aircraft; after all, even if a strengthened
design facility was found necessary, this could easily have been
done within the existing institutional infrastructure. But like
many instances in the past, the lack of integration between the
design agency (often the DRDO laboratory) and production
agency (HAL) would ultimately lead to time and cost overruns
and performance deficits. At one stage, there was a proposal to
transfer NAL to defence, which Valluri, with some justification,
states "would have been an unmitigated disaster, considering
how the DRDO laboratories were being run at that time."[4]

The lack of success on the implementation of the
recommendations by the C. Subramaniam Committee led Mrs.
Indira Gandhi, the then Prime Minister, to set up an Aerospace
Group on the advice of her Principal Secretary, Shri P.N. Haksar in
1976, with wide ranging terms of reference, including the possibility
of restructuring the organisational framework of aeronautics in
the country. The group consisted of Prof M.G.K. Menon, the
SA to the Defence Minister as the convenor, Defence Secretary,
Secretary Defence Production, the three Chiefs of Staff of the
Armed Forces, Professor Satish Dhawan, Secretary, Department
of Space, Dr. A. Ramachandran Secretary, Department of Science
and Technology, Air Marshal S.J. Dastur, Chairman HAL, and
Dr. V.S. Valluri, Director NAL, with Air Marshal Narasimhan as
the Secretary to the committee. Valluri writes that there were
"reservations from the Secretaries in the Defence Ministry from
the very beginning" when Air Marshal Narasimhan proposed an
organisation chart at the first meeting.[5]

The core problem was the extensive disjunctions between
various research, development and production agencies. To

overcome these, Dr. Valluri tried hard to pursue the case for an integrated Aeronautics Commission, as indeed had been pursued also by the IAF, especially Air Chief Marshal O.P. Mehra as the CAS. Unfortunately, a number of proposals for establishing an Aeronautics Commission to coordinate the various research, design and production facilities did not find favour with the decision-makers in South Block, the last one being an attempt in 2006 with the blessing of Dr. A.P.J. Abdul Kalam, then President of India (and the Supreme Commander of the Armed Forces). While the majority of scientists were in favour of an integrated Aeronautics Commission (on the model of the Space and Atomic Energy Commission) Dr. Valluri is candid in stating that even one Scientific Adviser to the Defence Minister opposed the concept on the grounds that with the creation of the Aeronautics Commission, the powers and office of the Scientific Adviser to the Defence Minister would be "weakened!" But Valluri was emphatic in stating that **without integration of the R&D institutions and the industry, there was precious little hope for ever achieving self-reliance.**[6]

LICENSED PRODUCTION

From one angle, the aircraft industry really grew and expanded through the licensed manufacture process, though it still had to meet the interim requirement of 45 squadrons. This essentially rested on the large supplies from the Soviet Union which in most cases led to licensed production. The payment for these weapons and systems was in Rupee terms though calculated against the Rouble assessed on the basis of a basket of currencies. The Soviet Union, in turn, purchased a large number of items for consumption ranging from rice, tea, hosiery, leather shoes, a wide range of critical medicines, and so on, which under the Cold War dispensation, they could not get from any other source. The Soviet needs were so great that progressively they sold weapons to India on long-term credit (for 12-17 years) at near nominal interest rates (2-odd percent per annum). Thus, the two countries established a mutually beneficial interdependence where, if anything, the Soviet Union was more dependent on India than the reverse. By 1988, the Soviet Union was India's largest trading partner. However, all the weapons were not bought from the Soviet Union and Europe was the primary alternative. The United States was unwilling to sell any arms, and barring some limited quantities of small arms, winter clothing and two radars, little came to India even after the Chinese War against India – and, hence, the US lost India at its critical time of need against the aggression by a Communist country against which the US had built up extensive military alliances across the globe.[7]

There is no explanation one can find that while not going up to the sanctioned force level of a 64-squadron force was not possible in 1963, it certainly was possible after the late 1970s and early 1980s (when the Air Force prematurely retired the HF-24 fleet of 141 serviceable aircraft) which by any consideration was still a new fleet equipping three squadrons with plenty to spare for additional squadrons. Apparently, the premature retirement of the HF-24 created space for the MiG-23BN/MiG-27 squadrons within the temporary sanction of the 35-combat squadron force while it could have provided the foundations of increasing the force to the authorised 50 combat squadrons.

But as forecast by the Subramaniam Committee, this licensed production process in **the post-Nehru period led to complacency and the breaking of the most important of the**

three threads of self-reliance: that of design and development.
HAL grew to become a massive facility, at one stage being listed
among the top 100 arms producing companies in the world,
but almost entirely on the basis of licensed manufactured
aircraft rather than its own designs in the post-Nehru era. We
will go into details later. But the central factor was that, like the
British Indian government had rendered the nascent aircraft
factory capable only of overhaul and did not allow design
and development of aircraft in HAL (then a private joint
venture) which was the original intention in 1940, the Indian
government of independent India, no doubt due to lack of
grasp of the critical aspects of the defence industry in South
Block, allowed the design and development capabilities built
up during the Nehru era to fizzle away and India has been
caught in the cycle of arms purchases, building them under
licence which led most Indians, including political leaders,
most military leaders and the public into a false sense of
capability which would receive repeated rude shocks when a
weapon system finished its design life and the process would
restart.

The MiG Complex
The MiG-21, which in the words of Bill Sweetman, "must
be judged as a classical combat aircraft"[8] in spite of its long
development period, was an outstanding Soviet design and
aircraft. A Mach 2 plus point defence interceptor (often termed
as a "manned rocket"), it remained under production for 28
years in 15 primary centres, including India, besides China,
until the Soviets cancelled the contract as the Sino-Soviet split
got wider, leaving China with the first variant, the MiG-21PF
which it later named as the J-7 (F/7 for the export version).
The aircraft had fought in more battles than any other aircraft

since World War II. Unfortunately, it was much maligned by our media in the late 1990s, without making any distinction between the five distinctly different aircraft (like the MiG-21/23BN/27ML/29 and the Mach-3 MiG-25 Foxbat) on account of flying accidents, without understanding the nature of the challenges.[9] The MiG-21 served India well for half a century and still flies in its upgraded version which consisted of at least six variants besides the three variants of the trainer. It was originally designed as a Mach-2+, very high altitude (22-km or so) interceptor armed with two K-13 air-to-air missiles for the air defence of the Soviet Union against a threat from the high-altitude US nuclear-armed heavy strategic bombers. In all, over 7,000 MiG-21s were manufactured and served with at least 33 countries, including China, where its Chinese derivative continues to be manufactured, and is in service, while a large number have been exported to developing, mostly Muslim, countries like Pakistan, Egypt, etc, besides other countries. The latest combat aircraft "jointly" developed by China and Pakistan, the JF-17 Thunder (FC-1 in China) is a clear derivative of the MiG-21 and was designed to use the MiG-29 engine.

The induction of the MiG-21 in India is studded with numerous important snippets of history of major power tensions. Sino-India relations had been on a clear downslide after 1959; at the same time, Sino-Soviet tensions had reached a high pitch by the end of the 1950s when Nikita Khrushchev and Mao Zedong were using almost abusive language in their meetings.[10] The Soviet leader had roundly criticised Mao for the gross mishandling of the Tibetan revolt and had accused Mao of facilitating the flight of the young Dalai Lama who should have been kept in Tibet. Mao almost burst a vein! By 1960, the Soviets had informed China of their intention to supply the MiG-21 to India; and China reacted violently. Moscow appeared to slow down with the process though most of the Indian Air Force leadership was also not in favour of the MiG-21 in spite of Defence Minister Krishna Menon's strong support to acquire Soviet weapons systems. New Delhi moved slowly because the possibilities of acquiring combat aircraft from the USA appeared to be increasing. In May 1962, it was reported that an agreement had been negotiated and concluded with the Soviets for the purchase and eventual manufacture of the MiG-21 in India.[11] One major factor in this process was the felt need to match Pakistan which had been supplied the Mach-2 high-performance F-104G Starfighter interceptor, which triggered the political value of acquiring the same from the United States, and, secondly, its speed at twice the speed of sound at high altitude, was a professional attraction besides the ability to have an aircraft matching in performance with the PAF.

People (including decision-makers) often forget that acquisition of high performance weapons automatically gets linked to high politics between states. The MiG-21 was to obviously become a major issue in international relations even though India was looking for a squadron of such aircraft. After China's war with India in late 1962, Prime Minister Nehru was willing to give up, or at least suspend, non-alignment when he wrote to President Kennedy asking for 12 squadrons of fighter aircraft and two squadrons of bombers to supplement the force level available with the IAF.[12] This was a major shift in the grand strategy of India and while the squadrons were not sent, extensive discussions between Washington and New Delhi started on arms sales to strengthen India's defences. Given the discussions taking place with the US at that time, the MiG deal with the Soviet Union was kept on hold.

Since the mid-1950s, Soviet-China relations had started to deteriorate and by 1959, Khrushchev and Mao were frequently using abusive language in the summit meetings of the two Communist allies.[13] Khrushchev repeatedly told Mao that he had decided to give MiG-21 aircraft to India along with whatever arms India desired. On the other hand, in the later half of 1962, the Cuban missile crisis had begun to hot up. The Soviet Union had deployed intermediate range ballistic missiles, MiG-23 aircraft and nuclear warheads to Cuba, America's backyard, in response to US deployment of Jupiter missiles in Turkey, the Soviet backyard. As the US-USSR tensions heated up, Khrushchev was worried about Mao stabbing him in the back while he was engaged in a high pressure high-risk nuclear confrontation with the United States. He, therefore, held a big banquet where he announced abiding "fraternal" friendship with China and even indicated that the Soviet Union would withhold the MiG-21 supplies to India. Mao, in turn, felt reassured that the Soviets would not support India and saw this as a signal for launching the war in October 1962.

The Sino-Indian War caught India grossly unprepared; but that is a different story. Subsequent discussions with the United States to acquire weapons, especially the F-104 (already supplied to Pakistan) and suitable fighters and radars went on with increased tempo after 1962. However, the United States, under pressure from Pakistan, declined to sell the F-104s. As regards fighters, it stressed again and again that the most suitable aircraft for India was the F-5 (while the F-86 had been supplied to Pakistan, and New Delhi was proposing the more capable F-4) and vague promises were made to provide technical assistance to improve the performance of the HF-24 Marut. But none of these and other proposals came to anything. Finally, by the time Nehru died in May 1964, New

Delhi had given up all hopes of building its arsenal with American assistance and turned to the pending Soviet offers. In the process, of course, the United States lost India to the Soviet Union quite consciously due to its infatuation with Pakistan as the bulwark of stability and support for US strategic interests. When the US decided to impose an arms embargo on Pakistan after its blatant and unprovoked invasion of India on September 1, 1965, following its covert war under Operation Gibraltar, Washington also extended the same to cover India, thus, equating the aggressor with the victim!

The Cuban missile crisis had wound down by the end of October 1962. The Soviet Union promptly criticised China for launching the war against India and, in a complete volte face, promised delivery of the MiG-21 and other arms required by India on priority. This may well have been a major factor in the Chinese declaration of a unilateral ceasefire and withdrawal from territories that they still claim (like the whole of Arunachal Pradesh). Incidentally, the Soviets had already supplied the MiG-21F to China in the mid-1950s along with the wherewithal to manufacture the aircraft. The Sino-Indian War marked the final split between the two countries. Hence, China was unable to graduate like India to later models of the MiG-21, and persistent Chinese efforts to upgrade the original version brought miniscule results till the arms technology pipeline to Russia opened again after the Soviet Union collapsed in 1991.

The year 1963-64 – the end of the Nehru era – started the extensive collaboration with the Soviet Union which agreed to production of its aircraft under licence in India. The first four aircraft were the MiG-21PF and were considered unsuitable. But the Soviets were already working on its follow-on model, the MiG-21FL, which had an airborne interception radar though only a ring-and-bead sight for air-to-ground weapon delivery. A batch of six aircraft was supplied in 1963 and the second in 1964 and assembled in India. The aircraft could carry two missiles under the wings and was powered by the Tumansky R11-F2 engine. On August 16, 1963, a new organisation named Aeronautics India Ltd. was established, surprisingly, with its head office in New Delhi and branch office in Bombay to manage and produce the MiG-21FL under licence. The manufacturing locations of the aircraft were selected at Ojhar at Nasik (in Maharashtra) with a new airfield not far from the Western Ghats for the airframe, Koraput (in Orissa) for the engine in the east (not very far from the Eastern Ghats!), and for the avionics and K-13 missiles, Balanagar (a suburb of Hyderabad), in the middle of the country. The three facilities, scattered across the wide swath of India, came to be termed as the MiG Complex under the Aeronautics India Limited.

The Koraput engine factory was not even connected by a railway line and the long trip to Nasik (and even MiG-21 squadrons as far away as Tezpur in the east and Pathankot in the west) to transfer manufactured engines for installation in the airframe and for/after overhaul/entailed transportation by hired civil trucks on narrow roads across the width of the country carrying the then sophisticated high-performance high-thrust jet engines! And the process has continued through the past five decades. It is obvious that our decision-makers in South Block had not understood the basics of high-technology arms production. Inevitably, in the early years, the Managing Director (who functions under the Chairman located at the HAL Corporate Office in Bangalore) of the MiG Complex had offices both at the HAL Corporate Office in Bangalore and at the Ojhar plant. Aeronautics India Ltd was renamed as Hindustan Aeronautics Ltd. (HAL) in 1964 after the Indian

Air Force's AMD (Aircraft Manufacturing Depot), the first industrial facility to begin manufacturing transport aircraft, was merged with the other complexes and brought under HAL on the same location where AMD was started in 1959 to manufacture transport aircraft by using the assets of one of the Base Repair Depots (BRDs) in Kanpur.

Manufacture of the MiG-21 at HAL started by 1967 with the early model MiG-21FL (with the Indian designation of Type 77) and the last of the MiG aircraft was manufactured twenty years later. HAL produced three fighter models of the MiG-21 at its factories. The IAF proposed many improvements (like the four under-wing hard points, improved gunsight for air-to-ground weapon delivery, etc.), but they were all incorporated in the MiG design bureaus (and not in HAL, for whatever reason) and new versions of the MiGs produced. From the MiG-21FL, HAL went onto its improved version which became the first multi-role model as the MiG-21M (with the Indian designation of Type 96) with four hard-points under the wings, two to carry fuel or all four to carry an assortment of air-to-air and air-to-ground weapons. Here we see a smaller but crucial example of the lack of understanding of aircraft and their manufacture by the decision-makers in South Block and/or in the corporate offices of HAL.

The first two squadrons of the new type, actually the MiG-21MF, were received in Completely Knocked Down (CKD) form and assembled in HAL. They were fitted with Tumansky R-13 engines with higher thrust. The engine was more powerful than the R-11 fitted to the MiG-21FL since the total weight of the aircraft, especially with additional weapon load, had increased. But the decision-makers failed to understand the simple logic that for combat aircraft, the thrust-weight ratio is a crucial factor in its performance. They opted for fitting the

R-11 engine (being manufactured at HAL's Koraput Division for the lighter MiG-21FL) in the heavier MiG-21M. The result was obviously inevitable and understood even by even a young rookie pilot/technician: the Air Force cooperated in the decision and received an underpowered MiG-21 capable otherwise of multi-role high performance. Through this act, HAL reduced a very capable multi-role combat aircraft (the MiG-21MF) to an underpowered MiG-21M for unexplained reasons except that of possible economies of scale and saving a small cost of the additional tools and parts needed to manufacture the R-13 engines instead of the R-11s which they had been doing for more than eight-odd years.[14] But it was certainly in accordance with HAL's larger tradition of producing underpowered aircraft. The IAF was forced to designate the aircraft essentially for a strike role leaving it potentially vulnerable in an air combat even with a MiG-21FL. It was only in the last few years that the remaining MiG-21Ms were fitted with R-13 engines.

In August 1976, HAL signed an agreement for licensed manufacture of the MiG-21bis, its R-25 power plant and associated equipment, avionics and accessories at its various divisions. The first aircraft was delivered from the assembly phase in November 1978. In fact, the IAF ordered the MiG-21bis in two lots, the first being placed in December 1976 and a subsequent one finalised in May 1981. The last of the MiG-21bis aircraft was delivered in March 1987. The first batch of Tumansky R-25 engines was received directly from the USSR, then being produced in progressive batches by March 1982, with a total of about 300 R-25-300 engines built by the engine division at Koraput.

By the time the manufacture of the MiG-21bis had commenced, the IAF had recognised two major weaknesses of the MiG fleet in the then operational-technological environment: the lack of a contemporary weapon suite and an accurate navigation and attack (nav-attack) system. This led to a number of modifications between 1977-1980 to integrate a contemporary weapon suite and an accurate inertial nav-attack system. The Matra Magic I close combat missile was integrated on the MiG-21bis, though only a portion of the fleet was fitted with this weapon. Ironically, a similar upgrade was undertaken two decades later, but with design and development being carried out by the Russians. A former IAF Deputy Chief of Air Staff has this to say:[15]

> The official reasons quoted in the files may be any, but I am firmly of the opinion that the main reason was that the Indian Air Force was not confident of taking it on its own, as it had no institutional organization to undertake any design and development work. HAL was just as ignorant (in spite of a design bureau integral to it at that stage) and the DRDO had never been involved with the MiG-21 fleet. Only if the IAF had not ignored the in-house design and development capability, (he added wistfully) it would have been the torch bearer among MiG-21 operating air forces.

This, indeed, is true since the IAF has stayed away from design and development of aircraft and their systems after the Indian Navy, its sister Service, established a Directorate of Warship Design, a Controller of Warship Construction and the Weapons Equipment and Systems Engineering Establishment, all in the Naval Headquarters. It is not surprising, therefore, that Indian Navy is well ahead of the Army and the Air Force in the indigenisation process of weapons and equipment. But as regards the IAF, during the reorganisation of Air HQ instituted by Air Chief Marshal P.C. Lall in late 1969, a Directorate for Projects was set up. In 1980-82, the IAF had also integrated the navigation attack and weapon aiming system for the Jaguar called the DARIN which made the Indian Jaguars far superior to those of the RAF and French Air Force. But in spite of these one-off steps, the fact remains that the IAF has not shown sufficient interest in creating in-house design and development capabilities or establishing a more direct vertical integration with the design bureaus of HAL.

By the early 1980s, the MiG-21 was flying with 475kg of ballast weight distributed in penny packets in different locations. This had resulted in weight savings, as new models of the equipment being installed in later versions of the aircraft and even replaced item-wise, weighed less. But the need to keep the centre of gravity in an aircraft so delicately balanced to give outstanding performance in the air required placing the necessary ballast weights mostly in the forward section of the aircraft ahead of the engine. Hence, the idea of upgrading the MiG-21bis (the designation "bis" in Russia implied the ultimate model or performance level) was never given up by the Air Force. In the early 1990s, Israel offered to upgrade the MiG further; but the Russians exercised their rights as prime manufacturers and designers. The upgrade of the MiG-21 had been receiving the attention of the decision-makers since the late 1970s even as the manufacture of the MiG-21bis began.

At one stage, 21 combat squadrons (out of the 35-squadron force then authorised) were equipped with the MiG-21 aircraft of different models. Between 1967 (when the MiG-21 production started at HAL under licence and 1987 when the production line was closed, HAL produced (assembled and progressive manufacture) a total of 862 aircraft (the breakdown is given below):[16]

MiG-21PF   12 (assembled)

MiG-21FL   180

MiG-21M/MF   200

MiG-21bis   220
MiG (assembled)   250 (including trainers)
                           862

On the face of it, with more than 700 aircraft manufactured in the country, there should not have been any serious difficulty to produce the LCA as originally conceived, that is, a modified MiG-21. The truth seems to be that by the end of the 1970s, HAL's design bureau had dissipated to the extent that it did not even take up design and development which was seen to be an urgent requirement at that time and was approved by the Prime Minister as Defence Minister.

The early MiG-21 had been priced at Rs. 40 lakh unit cost which had risen to around Rs. 69 lakh by the early 1970s (for the MiG-21MF). HAL's quoted price for this aircraft later was Rs. 1.12 crore (without weapons), making it one of the most cost-effective combat aircraft in the world. But after 1985, it was clear that the Soviet Union had begun to change under Gorbachev and his reforms. It was patently clear that as the Soviet system changed, so would its institutions and economic structures, and, hence, changes in the Soviet price structure were inevitable. This would inevitably have a great impact on Indian defence and defence expenditure. This author had argued for the necessity to take precautionary measures and even proposed reopening the MiG-21 manufacturing line in the mid-late 1980s so that the aircraft could be upgraded to completely new standards.

The collapse of the Soviet Union at the end of 1991 created enormous challenges for India since neither the Ministry of Defence nor HAL, used as they were to dealing with the formal agencies of the USSR, had any clear idea about the factories and facilities and their locations that were producing the systems, sub-systems, components and spare parts for the aircraft that constituted the backbone of the Indian Air Force. On the other hand, the tectonic development also resulted in a severe economic crisis in Russia and the former Soviet Union. While this implied a major challenge on how to maintain the IAF, it also opened a unique strategic opportunity to begin joint ventures for future aircraft and systems. While this approach was supported at the political level, it did not acquire any traction in HAL and DRDO, the two key agencies that had assumed roles far beyond what may be seen as appropriate. The IAF, which had kept itself aloof from involvement in design and development, paid a heavy price in low serviceability and reliability because of the lack of spare parts of aircraft being manufactured and overhauled in the country for the previous three decades.

It is in this context that DRDO announced its famous policy solution called the "Self-Reliance Initiative" (SRI) in 1995 to transform the Indian defence industry from 70:30 percent imports vs. indigenous content within 10 years. It was patently clear that this could at best apply to spare parts rather than to the complete defence industry as claimed since design, development and production of completely new systems across the board for the Air Force alone would take decades. Incidentally, the ten-year SRI was extended by another ten years in 2005 when it failed to make the slightest difference even in the spare parts regime. The major reason was that the Design Bureau of HAL, set up when the factory was established, was first emasculated during the pre-independence years, as shown in Chapter 2, and the fledgling bureau which had begun and designed the HT-2, HJT-16, HF-24, etc. had virtually been dissipated by the mid-1980s with the ad-hoc DRDO managed ADA having been created outside the manufacturing factory.

As regards jet engines for the MiG fleet, throughout the period since the factory was set up to produce R-11 engines for the MiG-21FL till now, no engine design bureau was established at Koraput which manufactured and repaired thousands of engines for MiG-21 aircraft essentially of four related designs for the MiG-21/27. The Bangalore Division, which has been producing engines for a large number of aircraft, also does not have an engine design and development organisation other than the GTRE (Gas Turbine Research Organisation) which is to develop and productionise the Kaveri engine for the LCA. This is perhaps the general policy of South Block since the Ordnance Factory Board, responsible for producing thousands of crores of rupees worth of ordnance material, also never had a design and development bureau. In fact, when I was responsible for flight safety at Air HQ, we found a major deficiency in the tail (breaking) parachutes for the Sukhoi SU-7 aircraft to slow down after landing. The Soviets insisted that they required a lead time of 24 months to manufacture additional parachutes. In order to conserve tail parachutes, we had to curtail flying training, with obvious implications. And yet, our defence industry sector produces thousands of parachutes for air-dropped supplies! On the other hand, HAL, Nasik Division, successfully developed the centre line drop tank of the MiG-29 air superiority fighter which is not even produced in India and is overhauled by the IAF Base Repair Depot that used to overhaul Su-7s. Indigenisation of the MiG-29's key parts and modifications is increasingly being carried out by the Nasik Division.

Aeronautics Committee
Going back a little, we need to recall that the Government of India set up an Aeronautics Committee in 1967 headed by C.

Subramaniam (and generally known as the "Subramaniam Committee") charged with a "comprehensive review of the research, development and production facilities in the aircraft and allied equipment field" in relation to the requirements in respect of aircraft and related equipment.[17] The committee submitted its report to the government in May 1969. (More about the committee's recommendations later). The committee focussed not only on R&D, but also on the relationship between licensed and indigenous production in the context of the force levels required/sanctioned. On the issue of threats and tasks, the IAF did not provide any information; and when the committee approached the Ministry of Defence in December 1968 for such information, the ministry took the view that:[18]

> ...the assessment of requirements for the Air Force was outside the terms of reference of the Aeronautics Committee. The Ministry of Defence stated, that given the requirements of the Air Force over a period of ten years, the Aeronautics Committee should recommend measures for the planned development of the aeronautics industry, so that these requirements can be met by manufacture within the country, in the shortest possible time and in the most economic manner.

Given this position taken by the Ministry of Defence, which should have spelt out the replies to the questions of force levels and strategy, it is not surprising that the IAF settled on the modification of the Gnat into the Ajeet soon after, but without a thorough empirical assessment of its cost-effectiveness in terms of flight safety record and range/payload comparison with the existing aircraft, the HF-24 Marut. The committee had gone on to state:[19]

> The purpose of the critical assessment is to ensure that the requirements are reasonably spelt out and not likely to be changed easily; that they take into account resources; that they are moderated, to the extent feasible, by the technological capability of the country .... Our defence

posture, defence positions and defence priorities cannot be taken at present value for the next decade. We have to deal with a changing situation. It is, therefore, important to recognise that the necessary exercises cannot be undertaken by any individual in any position. They have to be undertaken by organisations which have built up the necessary competence for the task. **It is possible that the hesitation of the Ministry of Defence to explore the basis of requirement arises from the handicap that none of the existing organisations has developed the competence to undertake the appropriate task** (emphasis added).

The committee's conclusions were very valid. Institutions and structures created as part of the Higher Defence Organisation (HDO) by Cabinet order in September 1947 had mostly been made non-effective. The Defence Committee of the Cabinet (DCC) the highest political authority on national defence policy and decision-making, had been set aside in 1962. The Joint Planning Committee, a key committee for military operational planning for the Chiefs of Staff Committee (COSC) had never been set up and it would be another 15 years after the Subramaniam Committee submitted its report that a Defence Planning Staff of the COSC was established but not fully manned by departments and institutions other than serving military officers. A Committee for Defence Planning composed of key Secretaries of the government had been created without the chiefs of the armed forces as members. There was serious opposition to the establishment of an Aeronautics Commission which could coordinate all efforts by bringing together, even informally, all the agencies and institutions dealing with aeronautics and aviation R&D and manufacture on one platform.

As regards the MiG-21, the committee urged that the MiG-21 should be further adapted and improved to meet the requirements of interceptors in the Seventies, and a "composite unit for the design, development and production of guided missiles should be quickly implemented."[20] Specifically, the committee "urged" that the MiG-21 should be "further adapted and improved to meet the requirements of interceptors in the seventies." In actual fact, the MiG-21 version, acquired soon after the Subramaniam Committee report was submitted, was a good multi-role combat aircraft till HAL/South Block decided to install the engine being manufactured in HAL for the MiG-21FL which was to be fitted with an earlier lower rated engine (the R-11 fitted on the lighter MiG-21FL) thus, unlike the HF-24 case, consciously creating an underpowered aircraft, contrary to the obvious urging of the high-powered Aeronautics Committee.

One of the critical conclusions of the Subramaniam Committee was that "research institutes were excluded from the planning process, that scientific expertise was not properly utilised and that productivity was low" in the aviation industry. Elsewhere, the committee commented that "if research establishments and the industry were involved in the formulation of weapons policy, their inventive skill could make a real difference."[21] By the same logic, the involvement of the IAF (like that of the Indian Navy), as the sole stakeholder in the final performance of the aircraft industry, at all levels of design and development of the aircraft for it, has remained crucial, but largely superficial involvement beyond the ASR (Air Staff Requirement) of which a number were issued in the 1970s but none produced even a prototype except for the Ajeet programme. The committee expressed its conclusion with respect to the desegregation of research, production and the military sector:[22]

> The principal aircraft requirements relate to the Air Force. Hence, the relationship between the Air Force as the indentor and the industry

is important; in fact, the success to meet the Air Force requirements by the manufacturer within the country depends upon complete understanding and (a) good working relationship between them.

However, little was done in this respect beyond the rare "steering committee" meetings. A logical first step in the implementation of this recommendation, accepted as part of the committee's report, would have at least led to the ADA society (when it was set up in the early 1980s) being headed by an IAF officer. However, the IAF was progressively isolated from the design, development and manufacture of aircraft in India. The classical example that stands out is that of withholding the design of the primary trainer to replace the already ageing HT-2 till the DGCA (an aviation regulatory authority of the government) ventured into designing aircraft in collaboration with the IIT – the IAF had to disengage from the LCA programme when the programme was redesignated as a "technology demonstrator" in the late 1980s and the first two aircraft were built and developed, with the prototype being produced only in the mid-1990s. On the other hand, the IAF kept issuing ASR through the 1970s, but little or no progress took place.

MiG-27ML Manufacture

As part of the ongoing reequipment and replacement of aircraft completing their design life, the IAF had evaluated the MiG-23MF for the air-to-air role in 1979, but it did not come up to expectations. The Soviets also offered the MiG-23BN, the dedicated strike aircraft, and this was recommended to be acquired. Hence, two squadrons of the MiG-23BN were assembled in India and entered service with the IAF in 1980-81. Talks also went on regarding the more advanced MiG-27ML version and these were acquired some time in 1983 for licensed manufacture. Pakistan had been interfering in Afghanistan since 1973 when Z.A. Bhutto had declared that Pakistan was not only a South Asian state but also a West Asian one. Soviet military intervention in Afghanistan in December 1979 rapidly and fundamentally altered the geo-political situation in the region, and inevitably India had to take the necessary counter-measures.

Pakistan had been seeking the A-7 from the US in the late 1970s but Washington was not willing to oblige because of the ongoing Pakistani clandestine nuclear programme. But with the Soviet military in Afghanistan, the picture changed rapidly and radically; and the US wanted Pakistan to be its "frontline state" in a covert war against the Soviets, hoping to reverse the Vietnam model. Finally, the US agreed to supply state-of-the-art weapons and equipment under its arms aid policies, including the F-16, then a very advanced aircraft. The Government of India made offers twice to Pakistan in the early 1980s to work together politically and diplomatically to get the Soviets to withdraw from Afghanistan. But both times, Islamabad rejected the offers.[23] At that stage, the IAF did not possess any aircraft with a modern interception radar leave alone a "look up, look down" capability and a matching "shoot up, shoot down" capability. DRDO, as the prime institution for applied research, had not even paid any attention to such a development project.

The Air Force had evaluated the Soviet MiG-23MF in 1979 but it had not come up to its expectations. With F-16s entering service with the Pakistan Air Force, it became a critical necessity to have some capability in this area. Moscow responded promptly to the Indian request and transferred two squadrons of the MiG-23MF; New Delhi, meanwhile, started negotiations with France for early acquisition of the Mirage

2000 which was still under development. I might add that, not certain of the specific type of MiG-23/27 aircraft and its systems acquired by India during those crucial years, the CIA and other Western intelligence agencies quickly picked up a strong interest and launched covert operations in India to get as much information on the MiG-23/27 as possible!

The MiG-27ML programme began in the mid-1980s—they came from Irkutz in Siberia in CKD form initially. Production of the MiG-21 bis was supplemented at HAL, Nasik, by the follow-on M1G-27ML programme and for a few years, even as the last MiG-21s were being completed, the first batches of the MiG-27s were being produced, this unique side-by-side structure continuing till March 1987, and from then onwards, the swing-wing tactical fighter occupied the HAL, Nasik, production lines exclusively for the next ten years.

After the last MiG-27ML was rolled out from the production line at Ojhar in March 1997, there had been no new aircraft production although its routine activity of overhaul of MiG-21s and MiG-27s has gone on with an average 60 of the former and 12 of the latter being undertaken each year, with over 1,100 aircraft overhauled since the 1970s. The extensive infrastructure of the Nasik aircraft factory was involved only in overhaul, like HAL had been pushed into in 1942.

Jaguar Tactical Strike Aircraft
In 1979, India signed a contract for the purchase of the Jaguar dedicated strike aircraft improperly named DPSA (Deep Penetration Strike Aircraft), a designation originally meant for the single heavy bomber squadron approved by the Cabinet in the IAF force structure in 1963, for which the Soviet long-range bomber was actually evaluated in 1971. The Jaguar proposal had been in the making for a long time and there were concerns

about its single role and incapacity for air combat and limited operational ceiling. The agreement stipulated direct import of 45 aircraft (for two squadrons) and licensed manufacture of another 110 aircraft at HAL, with progressive increase in indigenous content in it.

However, the Jaguar contract was revised in 1980 and plans for production were suspended. Instead, the government began to consider acquisition of the Mirage 2000 multi-role combat aircraft on similar terms though at a somewhat higher price. The contract for the Mirage was signed in 1982 for direct import of 45 aircraft with an option of local manufacture of 110 aircraft. This resulted in the Soviet Union, which had been denying the existence of the MiG-29 till that time, to agree to provide some basic details asserting that the aircraft was still under development and, hence, could not be offered for any trials or evaluation. The one-year option for manufacturing the Mirage-2000 was extended by another year. The Soviet Union then offered the MiG-29 for evaluation by IAF test pilots who found it to be an excellent aircraft though only for air-to-air warfare with no air-to-ground capability at that stage.

The Jaguar aircraft continued to be manufactured in HAL under licence in small numbers of 10-15 at a time. Ultimately, over 115 Jaguars were built in HAL. However, the piecemeal approach denied us the advantage of economies of scale in terms of indigenisation. The Air Force was satisfied with the aircraft since indigenous upgrade of the NAVWAS (Navigation and Weapon Attack System) leading to replacement by the DARIN system met the operational requirements.

Sukhoi Su-30MKI
The government signed an agreement for the development of the Sukhoi's Su-30MK to Su-30MKI standard in 1995 to

meet the Air Force needs for long range strike, including with nuclear weapons and BVR air combat capabilities. Meanwhile, the Russian supplied 40 Su-30MK aircraft to be later retro-modified. At close to 39 tons maximum all-up weight and 8 tons of armament, the two cockpit aircraft and state-of-the-art avionics is one of the best aircraft in the world. It is certainly capable of providing air dominance (both in air-to-air as well as air-to-surface dominance) with advanced strike capabilities which would be equipped with the 300-km range PJ-10 Brahmos Mach-3 cruise missile produced by the joint Indo-Russian project.

The actual development of the Su-MKI started in 2000 with a contract to supply 140 aircraft manufactured to proprietary Indian specifications. The first indigenously assembled aircraft from HAL, Nasik Division, entered service with the IAF in 2004. Since then, more aircraft have been ordered and the total inventory of the IAF is expected to be around 272 aircraft by 2018, constituting the single largest type of aircraft in service by that time and, hence, the IAF primary frontline multi-role combat aircraft. The development includes state-of-the-art avionics developed by Russia, India and Israel. India is planning to equip the aircraft with the Russian Zhk-AE Active Electronically Scanned Array (AESA) radar which can track 30 targets and engage six at the same time.[24] For its BVR air-to-air capability, it is equipped with a series of missiles with ranges varying from 70 to 130 km besides the short range R-73 with a range of 30 km. India is engaged in joint development of the Novstar KS-172 air-to-air missile with a range of 400 km (which the Russians describe as an "AWACS Killer"). The production rate of the aircraft has also been raised from 10 to 14 aircraft a month in order to recoup the shortfall in the IAF combat squadron force.

DIRECT IMPORT OF MANUFACTURED AIRCRAFT

The robust expansion of the Air Force from 25 squadrons to 45 squadrons (35 combat and 10 transport squadrons) authorised in 1963 in view of the northern frontier having come alive in 1961 followed by the Sino-Indian War of 1962 demanded great urgency. The US government provided prompt assistance in positioning its C-130 transport squadron at New Delhi to carry stores (winter clothing for the troops, some personal weapons and wireless sets, etc.) to Leh and other places for the Army. For the IAF, they had agreed to provide two surveillance and interception radars. The government had initially sought to acquire combat aircraft from the United States. Discussions dragged on till 1965 and the US, under pressure from Pakistan, was not willing to provide the F-104G Starfighter supersonic interceptor to India. It was also lukewarm on the issue of assistance to provide a suitable engine for the HF-24 Marut which would enable it to reach its designed performance of Mach-2 capability. The US kept insisting that the F-5 Freedom Fighter would meet IAF requirements. The IAF already possessed the Mystere and Hunter aircraft and the F-5 would only have added another type without in any way enhancing the operational capability of the Air Force.

The Soviet Union had already offered the MiG-21 in 1961. However, it was seen to have very limited utility in India as a pure supersonic interceptor armed with early models of air-to-air infra-red homing missiles. But when the US continued to dilly dally, it was decided to acquire the aircraft and manufacture it under licence, as noted earlier. In 1965, the US applied sanctions on all arms supplies to India consequent to Pakistan's aggression against India. The two radars were caught in this process and it took many years before they could be made operational by obtaining different parts from other sources. In order to fill the gap in force level, it was also decided to acquire a couple of squadrons of the Sukhoi Su-7 strike aircraft in 1967 directly from the Soviet Union and there were no plans to manufacture these in the country.

Mirage 2000H

As noted earlier, in 1982, in response to the massive US arms aid to Pakistan which included 42 F-16A/B high-technology aircraft, the government sanctioned the acquisition of two squadrons' (45 aircraft) worth of French Mirage-2000H multi-role combat aircraft. While the option to manufacture the aircraft in India was retained for one year and again extended by one year, it was never exercised. Two additional squadrons were raised in 1985 to be equipped with the imported aircraft, raising the force level to 37 combat squadrons. The aircraft has been serving well with the Air Force and particularly played a crucial role in day and night attacks on the Pakistan Army and its logistics dumps on our side of the Line of Control during the Kargil War in the summer of 1999.

MiG-29 and MiG-29K

As noted earlier, the Soviets offered the MiG-29 for trials in 1983. These were found to be very suitable for air-to-air warfare. Consequently, two squadrons worth of MiG-29s were acquired directly in 1986 and one more was acquired in 1993. It was generally expected that licensed manufacture of the MiG-29 would start in India, though HAL was keen for a linear approach that should follow the production line of the MiG-27 being completed. By that time, the Soviet Union had disintegrated. And while this opened up enormous and historic opportunities for joint ventures for design, development and manufacture of aircraft, engines and weapon systems, this did not get the support of DRDO and other decision-making levels in spite of the political authorities showing a high degree of keenness. The IAF leadership, in fact, saw this as an opportunity to access the Western market for arms. But the MiG-21 reached the end of its design life and no replacements meant decline in the combat force level. This tragically, based on an oversimplified "doctrine of necessity," led to the view in the early 1990s that the IAF should go in for force multipliers and not worry too much about the force level. Fortunately, the Russians extended the design life of the MiG-21 airframe, thus, postponing the crisis for a few years till the force level started an unplanned downslide in the early 2000s and has continued coming down from 39.5 squadrons to 28-odd squadrons by 2010. And it may take another 15-odd years to get back to the currently approved force level of 39.5 squadrons before we can start to move to the promised 42 squadrons or the Cabinet approved force level of 50-combat squadrons.

The fact that at that stage the MiG-29 was not modified for the strike role further influenced the thinking even to the extent that New Delhi showed no desire to acquire the MiG-29s at a marked down price of over 84 brand new aircraft ordered by Soviet Air Force that now it no longer required. And yet it was clear to even rookie pilots that an air superiority fighter can always be modified for the air-to-ground role with its high thrust-weight ratio while the reverse was not true.

INDIGENOUS DESIGN AND DEVELOPMENT

It is said that those who can't remember their past will be condemned to repeat it. This is true in the field of aeronautics during the past sixty years or so in our country.

— Dr. S.R. Valluri[25]

As noted in the earlier chapters, India had been systematically deindustrialised on the strength of Europe's own industrialisation once the Industrial Revolution had set in. By the beginning of World War II, there was a smattering of industry in the country, but all in the civil sector. No defence industry worth its name existed. The ambitious attempt by Walchand Hirachand to build an aircraft industry at Bangalore in collaboration with an American as a private venture strongly supported by the Maharaja of Mysore was soon to be not only taken over by the British Indian government, but forced to regress to mere overhaul and repair of mostly aircraft engines and some aircraft for the US Far Eastern Air Forces after Pearl Harbour. Even the arms industry for the infantry was pathetically inadequate: while India fielded the history's largest volunteer Army with 2.6 million men on the battlefront, even they were equipped with rifles and ammunition which mostly came from other colonies like Australia, New Zealand and South Africa. The general level of machine-based industry was extremely limited.

It is in this context that we need to see the ambitious attempt to design and develop a state-of-the-art multi-role combat aircraft, the LCA, three decades ago which has yet to enter service as of end-2010. As if to prove the theory of unintended consequences of carefully planned schemes, the LCA was not meant to be so. The original plan triggered by the Operations Branch of Air HQ in 1980 was to evolve a light and low cost fighter to replace the MiG-21 whose early model, the MiG-21FL, was scheduled to retire from service beginning 1985-86. The concept was to modify the front fuselage of the MiG-21 to achieve four goals essentially with the goal of making the aircraft more capable for low level battlefield operations:

- Shift the air intake from the aircraft nose intake to side intakes. The sophisticated management of airflow so critical for supersonic flight at above 14-km altitude was no longer critical for a fighter to be used at low levels and, in fact, could reduce the accidents due to nose cone malfunctioning.
- The redesigned nose could accept a new better radar for air interception, possibly from Western sources.
- The above would make it possible to provide a cockpit with much greater visibility for the pilot and allow for space inside the aircraft to install an air-conditioning system in the cockpit (The MiG-21 did not have a cool air system leave alone air-conditioning and cockpit temperatures at low level flight could easily touch 70 degrees Celsius!).
- And last, but not the least, the MiG-21 was already flying with 475 kg of ballast weight in small quantities dispersed mostly in the area ahead of the engine. This could be utilised for internal fuel and, thus, extend its range.

But what the Air Staff Target (AST) for the LCA became in the early 1980s was for an aircraft that would be unstable and, hence, very highly manoeuvrable, which, in turn, necessitated the Fly-By-Wire (FBW) controls, very high rate of turn, full control over the aircraft even under very high angle of attack, and so on, with a powerful engine to provide a high thrust-weight ratio in excess of one. Such an aircraft was way beyond a simple though substantive redesign of the front section of a MiG-21. But even when the ASR was finalised after feasibility studies of the AST were carried out consequent to the LCA integrated design team, with consultations with BAe, Marcel Dassault, Dornier, MBB and Italians as potential partners with the LCA programme,[26] the all-up weight of the aircraft remained unchanged. In turn, this necessitated extensive use of composites which technology had been developed at NAL although a larger autoclave had to be imported. It appears the Soviets were not involved for reasons difficult to identify or fathom, but probably because the design concept had moved far beyond the original thinking of a modified MiG-21. Perhaps both designs could have been pursued, the MiG-21 design based on collaboration with the Soviet Union and the other more independently, with collaboration with Western aircraft designers. This would have given us an incremental approach with reasonable assurance that at least one design would result in a usable, operational and effective LCA and low cost. It is worth remembering that in January 1980s, HAL's marked up unit cost of the MiG-21 sale to the IAF was Rs. 1.12 crore.

To digress a bit, the Chinese FC-1 programme and its later version of the China-Pakistan joint project of the JF-17 is based on the MiG-21 design and is reportedly helped by Russian designers and fitted with the R-29 engine that powers the MiG-29. The cost as usually cited in 2009-10 public sources of the JF-17 (Thunder in the PAF) is around US$ 5 million (approximately Rs. 22 crore per unit). The Indian LCA cost for 20 aircraft contracted by the IAF in March 2006 came to approximately Rs. 135 crore per unit.[27] Weapons integration (not to mention the cost of the weapons) would no doubt add to the costs. One wonders whether the LCA would be six times more capable than the PAF's JF-17.

But to get back to the vicissitudes of aircraft design, it appears a tussle started among the scientific community on who would undertake the project. It was apparently taken for granted that the HAL design bureau would not. In fact, the HAL design bureau's offer to design even the AJT had been dropped for reasons difficult to fathom. Valluri writes that LCA studies by the integrated team had continued though with notable centrifugal pressures which also became an issue in the media in those years. As per Valluri, he and the then Scientific Adviser to the Defence Minister, Dr. V.S. Arunachalam were present at a meeting of the LCA integrated design team called in the office of the Secretary, Defence Production, Mahesh Sareen, "to discuss the organisation for design and development of the LCA. It was unanimously agreed that the Aeronautical Development Agency (ADA) should be created to handle the LCA programme."[28] It was also unanimously agreed that its responsibility would be to fund, manage, and monitor the LCA programme and that it should be a "lean organisation which could be closed at short notice" implying that it was not only ad-hoc but was also an interim arrangement. Valluri goes on to say, "The idea was that HAL would be the prime contractor, with NAL, ADE, GTRE, and other organisations working in subcontractor mode, under the auspices of ADA."

ADA was registered as a society. Valluri formally took over as Director General ADA on July 2, 1984, with the rank of a Secretary to the Government of India and he brought in Raj Mahindra to manage the design work of the LCA. He had estimated in 1983 that the first LCA prototype would fly in 1991, and six prototypes would be required to complete the flight tests in about three years and production could then start around 1994. The cost of the programme up to that stage was estimated to be Rs. 1,250 crore (and every year of delay would add Rs. 150 crore to the cost). As things started to move forward, difference of opinions and personalities also emerged, leading to Valluri and Raj Mahindra both leaving ADA in November 1985. However, the design work started off with great energy under Dr. Kota Harinarayan whose own enthusiasm was infectious. The ADA overall was headed by

Dr. V.S. Arunachalam, the Scientific Adviser to the Defence Minister.

Differences between the ADA and Air Force on the design and its performance grew by 1989 till a committee was appointed to resolve them. The result was that from then on, the Air Force detached itself from the LCA programme in view of its lack of confidence in the promises being made. The LCA then was left as a "technology demonstrator" and after the first prototype had flown, the Air Force was willing to rejoin the programme in spite of its serious concerns about the LCA's ability to meet the ASR. The LCA has undertaken a total of 1,452 test flights since its technology demonstrator first flew on January 4, 2001, and the first prototype flew on November 25, 2003. Incidentally, the LCA still does not meet the IAF ASR on various counts. The LCA was to be powered by the indigenously developed Kaveri engine which is far from ready. Additional problems have cropped up due to higher weight than the design visualised and, hence, the need for a more powerful engine to provide the design thrust weight ratio in order to obtain the requisite performance. The Ministry of Defence has issued the RFP (Request for Proposal) for a suitable engine for the LCA. It remains to be seen whether further modifications to the airframe would be required to match the selected engine, with inevitable further testing.

It is, indeed, surprising that we ignored the lessons of the first (and last) combat aircraft designed in India, the HF-24 Marut. The central reason why the aircraft could not be used to its full potential in spite of an excellent airframe design with clean lines was because of the lack of a suitable engine. And South Block dithered in paying the requisite sum for the development of the engine which was meant to be installed in the aircraft. I recall raising the issue of lessons of the past from the HF-24 and others with Dr. V.S. Arunachalam, the Scientific Adviser to the Defence Minister in the late 1980s and early 1990s: the failure to design an aircraft around a tried engine, the problem of almost all HAL designs ending up with higher than designed weight thus making the aircraft underpowered, and so on. But somehow we have not been able to learn from past mistakes.

Notes

1. C. Subramaniam Committee Report 1968, pp. 67-68, cited in Chris Smith, *India's Ad-hoc Arsenal: Direction or Drift in Defence Policy?* (Oxford, SIPRI and Oxford University Press, 1994), p. 167.

2. S.R. Valluri, *Events in Life: Struggle for Self-Reliance in Aeronautics* (Private publication, 2007), p. 79.

3. Ibid., p. 81.

4. Ibid., p. 87.

5. Ibid., p. 86.

6. Ibid., p. 92.

7. On the other hand, the US, conscious of the Sino-Soviet split that came to the fore in 1962 during the Sino-Indian War, began to lead US strategic thinking to start the process of reshaping its relationship with China, concretised after the Sino-Soviet border war in 1969.

8. Bill Sweetman, *Soviet Military Aircraft* (London: Hamlyn Publishing Group, 1981), p. 87.

9. The nomenclature of the variety of aircraft under the acronym MiG stands for the names of the designers Mikoyan and Gurevich.

10. For example, see CWIH Project, *The Cold War in Asia*, "Khrushchev and Mao Discuss Current Political Situations in Tibet, India, Indonesia and Taiwan," March 10, 1959.

11. *The Times of India*, May 6, 1962. See also *The Hindu*, May 9, 1962.

12. Major General D.K. Palit, *War in the High Himalayas: The Indian Army in Crisis, 1962* (New Delhi: Lancer International, 1991), p. 342.

13. See CWIH Project at http://wilsoncenter.org/index.cfm?topic_id=1409&fuse action=va2...

14. Considering that Soviet weapons were paid for in Rupee-Rouble trade, the issue of shortage of hard currency in India did not arise.

15. Personal conversation, August 31, 2010.

16. Alka Sen, *Glimpses into Indian Aviation History 1910-1997* (Bombay: Indian Aviation News Services Pvt, 1998), p. 364.

17. *The Hindustan Times*, November 11 and December 6, 1967.

18. Subramaniam Committee 1968, cited in Smith, n. 1, p. 166.

19. Ibid., p. 167.

20. Raju G.C. Thomas, *The Defence of India: A Budgetary Perspective of Strategy and Politics* (New Delhi: Macmillan Company of India, 1978), p. 194.

21. Smith, n. 1, p. 168.

22. Ibid., p. 168.

23. Author's discussions with Mr Agha Shahi, the Foreign Minister of Pakistan (in 1980), in June 1988 and again in July 1996 in Islamabad.

24. Neelam Mathews, "India Eyes Su-30 AESA Upgrade," *Aviation Week and Space Technology*, October 8, 2010.

25. Valluri, n. 2, p. 78.

26. Ibid., p. 89.

27. Seventeenth Report of the Standing Committee on Defence (14th Lok Sabha) titled *In Depth Study and Critical Review of Hindustan Aeronautics Limited (HAL)*, May, 2007, p. 34

28. Valluri, n. 2, p. 94.

6

Transport Aircraft
The Neglected Sector?

I have often said, for best results, industrial research is best done by industry in industry.

— Dr. Atma Ram, DG, CSIR[1]

While HAL's record in designing and developing combat aircraft has been patchy at best and inexplicably ignored, especially after licensed production of Soviet aircraft, it has not taken any interest in transport aircraft design and development. Very recently, some effort was made by NAL (National Aerospace Laboratories), Bangalore (now Bengaluru), one of the national laboratories under the Ministry of Science and Technology established in the early years of independence to undertake basic research in aeronautics. Unfortunately, this twin-engine transport aircraft, with a capacity for 18 passengers, crashed not long after its first flight. Meanwhile, development and testing of the Saras is going on. NAL has now launched a project to design and develop an 80-90 seat transport aircraft. Since NAL is essentially a research laboratory, it can be presumed that the eventual manufacture of such an aircraft would be undertaken by HAL (at its Kanpur factory, more than 1,600 km away from NAL) or a new production facility would be set up.

It is, indeed, surprising that HAL never attempted to design a transport aircraft. Normally, most aircraft industries have placed special emphasis on transport aircraft. In earlier periods, most of the bomber designs evolved out of transport aircraft which were used mostly for commercial purposes, thus, offsetting the investments in design and development of transport aircraft against the civil market. At the same time, military aircraft, from the primary trainer to the high performance combat aircraft, involve much higher technologies, near-zero tolerance in precision and performance, and above all, are time sensitive due to operational imperatives. Compared to that, the transport aircraft, even for military uses, have much more relaxed time and performance requirements. Now, with the introduction of aerial refuelling, the requirement of tanker aircraft has increased significantly and so has that for the Airborne Early Warning and Control (AEW&C) and Airborne Warning and Control System (AWACS).

With the progressive expansion of the IAF, its needs for transport aircraft also grew. The 1963 Cabinet approval for a 64-squadron force would have required 14 transport squadrons (which would have required over 170 frontline aircraft), besides a large number of training units and Communication Flights and provision for aircraft on overhaul, repair and possible losses in peace and war. Even the interim sanction of 45 squadrons required 10 squadrons of frontline transport aircraft for heavy lift, medium tactical airlift and the odd light communication duties besides the training units and the Air HQ Communication Squadron and various Communication Flights and survey requirements, etc. A brief summary of transport aircraft that have been/ are in service in the IAF (including in the earlier Nehru era), would help us to get some idea of actual requirements and usage:

Table 6.1

Type	Quantity	Method of Acquisition
Pre-1962		
Dakota C-47/DC-3	100 plus	Mostly reconstructed from WWII old/damaged stocks
Packet C-119G	79	Direct purchase from USA
Avro HS-748	89	Licensed manufacture (British)
Avro HS-748	80	Licensed manufacture (British)
DHC Caribou	18	Direct purchase from Canada
DHC Otter	21	Direct purchase from Canada
Post-1962		
An-12B	41	Direct purchase from USSR
IL-14	24	Direct purchase from USSR
IL-76/78	60 app	Direct purchase from USSR/FSU
An-32	115	Direct purchase from USSR
Dornier 228	155	Licensed manufacture (Germany)

In addition, the Air HQ Communication Squadron (for VIP/VVIPs) always had a complement of different types of aircraft ranging from the Tu-124 to the present Embraer, Avro-748, etc. Nearly seven Communication Flights used the Avro for decades. Barring the Dakotas which started being used from 1947 onward, and the Fairchild Packet C-119G [imported from the United States, which entered service starting 1954 and were modified with an Orpheus jet engine pack on top of its fuselage (in India) to make it capable of flying over the high Himalayas for supply dropping], all other aircraft entered service from the end 1950s. It is, therefore, surprising that the Aeronautics Committee headed by C. Subramaniam recommended that airliners were to be imported, implying that transport aircraft for domestic airlines would also be imported rather than manufactured in India. Either way, the reality was that a reasonably large number of transport aircraft was required even in the 1960s. The bulk of these aircraft were employed in supply dropping and landing in the Himalayas for the Army and civil population since few, if any, roads exited in the 4,000-km-long Himalayan ranges.

As may be seen from Table 6.1, no transport aircraft has been designed in India so far by HAL or DRDO. This may be attributable to the influence of the Blackett Report and/ or the recommendations of the high-powered Aeronautics Committee headed by C. Subramaniam in 1967-68 that India should rely on imported airliners. How far this applied to military transport aircraft, especially since the Avro was already under licensed production at the time that the Aeronautics Committee was deliberating on, and finalised, its report, and the enterprise should have led to the next step, that of design of a transport aircraft, is not clear. Less than five years after the 1962 War, when the nation was still under the national Emergency declared in 1962, air supply dropping was the primary means of supplying the Army deployed on the border across the high Himalayas since the roads were just about beginning to be built. In fact, the IAF had undertaken the Herculean task of dropping supplies at virtually four times the available capacity in 1962. One would have imagined that design and development of a transport aircraft to meet our specific requirements of air supply in the Himalayas would have been a high priority after 1962.

There may be a view that India was a poor country and its people could not afford the luxury of transport aircraft. But the sheer size of India's territory would indicate the necessity for air travel and, hence, of a reasonable number of transport aircraft for military and civil uses. As it is, there was enough traffic to bear the cost of operations of airlines. It may be of interest to note that after the end of World War II a large number of private airlines had cropped up, using war surplus transport aircraft (mostly Dakotas) refurbished for carrying passengers. By 1950, when nearly 80 percent of the population was below the poverty line, 18 such airlines were operating on non-scheduled routes and even by 1952, 14 private airlines were operating across the vast expanse of Indian territory. These airlines employed 291 Indian and 38 foreign pilots.[2] It is in this context that the manufacture of the first transport aircraft was attempted, interestingly in what was essentially an IAF unit and airfield, headed by Air Vice Marshal Harjinder Singh, OBE, the AOC-in-C Maintenance Command, IAF, at Kanpur.

LICENSED PRODUCED AIRCRAFT

Avro (Hawker Siddley-BAe) HS-748

The first transport aircraft manufactured in India was under licence, of the new design by Hawker Siddley, later merged with BAe (British Aerospace) named Avro HS-748. The process of setting up this endeavour was even more unique than the novelty of transport aircraft manufacture; and the main credit for it goes to two mavericks, Shri Krishna Menon, the then Defence Minister, and Air Vice Marshal Harjinder Singh CBE, the AOC-in-C Maintenance Command, IAF, located at Kanpur (and the first *Hawai Sipahi* of the IAF in 1932). That the Avro 748 medium transport aircraft was to have mixed success was not, in any way, to dilute the boldness of the decision taken at the time.

Harjinder Singh had become a legend in the IAF in the early years of the IAF itself because of his ability to undertake what appeared to be impossible tasks of maintenance and repair successfully, mostly in record time. By 1948, he had been promoted to Group Captain rank and posted to command the Air Force Station at Kanpur where he had been the spirit behind the resurrection of 50-odd Liberators from the junkyard in which they had been dumped by the British. Harjinder was promoted to the rank of Air Commodore as the AOC of the newly raised Maintenance Command, IAF, at Kanpur, where he had reconstructed a private Bonanza aircraft. Encouraged by Krishna Menon, he also designed and built Kanpur-1, a light communication aircraft at Kanpur. This sowed the seeds of licensed manufacture of Avro transport aircraft.

An IAF team, led by AVM Harjinder Singh had proceeded to the UK on August 10, 1959, for detailed interaction with Avro at Manchester and returned after a month. To quote: "After the six weeks we were in England, some of which were spent with A.V. Roe & Co. in Manchester, the others in London, coordinated by the Air Adviser, Group Captain (later Air Chief) H. Moolgavkar, we felt fully familiarised with the manufacturing schedule of the Avro. We were all set to start work on the project as soon as we returned to India but found there was still opposition to this aircraft and it was not till 23 January, 1960, that the foundation stone of the Aircraft Manufacturing Depot (AMD) at Kanpur was laid by the Commander-in-Chief and Chief of the Air Staff, Subroto Mukerjee."

The organisation for undertaking this project, called the Aircraft Manufacturing Depot (AMD) in tune with the other depots for repair, etc. was created at Kanpur in 1959. The arrangements for licensed manufacture of the Avro were finalised. The AMD was essentially manned by IAF technicians and for this purpose, Harjinder had asked for 50 Warrant Officers and 1,000 airmen and lascars to be seconded from the Air Force.[3] While this number would take quite some time, the technicians from the Air Force all comprised high quality manpower. This was boosted subsequently by engineers from the civil sector increasing the strength to over 5,000 persons.

The AMD was formally established as the first (and only) IAF Aircraft Manufacturing Depot (AMD) on January 23, 1960, initially comprising four empty storage hangars which belonged to Nos. 1 and 4 Base Repair Depots (BRDs) of the IAF at Chakeri aerodrome, Kanpur. Air Vice Marshal Harjinder Singh has stated in his memoirs:[4]

> Towards the end of 1958 and the early part of 1959, we began considering the purchase of transport aircraft to replace our old Dakota fleet. Meetings were held at all levels – in the Planning Commission, in the Cabinet and in Defence Ministry – and much heat was generated, not always for the right reasons.
>
> In the end, Krishna Menon's arguments overcame all the prejudices. It was on June 27, 1959, that the decision was taken to manufacture the Avro 748 in India. Typical of Menon, he was thereafter all impatience and wanted the first Indian-made aircraft to take to the air on the next Republic Day Parade – in other words, in less than seven months time!

The Avro 748 was then still at the development stage (as indeed were the Gnat light fighter, the Vijayanta tank, etc. that India took on to further develop[5]) with the A.V. Roe Company in the Manchester area of Britain. With the indefatigable efforts and foresight of AVM Harjinder Singh, and the strong support of Krishna Menon, the government concluded an agreement for the licensed manufacture of the Avro 748 in India. Even as the first prototype of the aircraft flew in England on June 24, 1960, metal on the first aircraft had already been cut on May 12, 1960, at the AMD, Kanpur. Simultaneously, decisions were taken to locally fabricate the majority of jigs and tooling for series production in two hangars vacated for the production of the aircraft. Avro personnel were also brought in to assist in the manufacture of the first aircraft almost at the same time as the parent company began production. The first aircraft assembled at AMD, Kanpur (wholly from imported components) was test flown on November 1, 1961, by (then Flight Lieutenant) Group Captain Kapil Bhargava at Chakeri. The first British production aircraft had flown, just two months earlier, on August 30, 1961.

By end 1961, all flying trials required for certification of the Avro 748 had been completed, a transport category Certificate of Airworthiness was awarded on January 9, 1962, and production deliveries began in the same month. The Hawker Siddeley Board had approved the construction of an initial batch of 10 aircraft, plus long lead time items for another 10. Since that time, the production commitment has been constantly "topped up" in the light of the back-log of firm orders plus projected future sales. The first order actually came from the Government of India which was meant for the IAF. The Indian production line was intended to satisfy the requirements of primarily the Indian Air Force and, to a lesser extent, Indian Airlines Corporation. The major weakness in the aircraft was that it was not capable of paradropping supplies or paratroopers though very soon, the IAF would be engaged in a major air supply chain for our troops, moving up across a 4,000-odd-km border in the Himalayas to supply the Army (and the civilian population) since hardly any roads existed. If this aspect had been kept in mind – and one must admit that tension on the Sino-Indian border had been increasing since 1959—perhaps a transport aircraft which could be effective in air-dropping supplies and troops might have been a better choice, if one was available. However, the inventory of the C119G Packet and the old work-horse, the Dakota, probably shaped the decision to go in for the Avro.

Soon after completion of the initial certification trials, the second prototype was converted to Series 2 standard with the RR Dart R Da 7 of 1910 shp and resumed flying in this configuration on November 6, 1961. It was used to obtain certification of the Series 2 (in October 1962, which then became a company demonstrator). The Series 2 very soon became the most important production version, with only 23 Series I aircraft being completed, including the first five aircraft from the Kanpur assembly line.

By sheer ingenuity and improvisation, the AMD engineers had converted the bare hangars into an aircraft production factory, having embarked upon an extensive programme of locally manufacturing most of the jigs and tools, reclaiming machines that had been disposed off earlier, utilising surplus stocks, and buying second- hand machine tools, thus, hugely saving foreign exchange. Complicated jigs and tools were fabricated indigenously from die outset, saving not only money but creating massive training-on-the-job opportunities for the skilled, largely serving or retired Air Force technical personnel. Maintaining close liaison and links with the Manchester plant, AMD proceeded with manufacture of the Series 1 aircraft, thus, saving much time and funds. A total of five Series 1 aircraft was assembled from imported components, and the second Avro 748 (named after "Jumbo" Majumdar) flew on March 13, 1963.

To begin with, the total personnel strength at the AMD was very modest – a few hundred – but with full series production, some 5,000 jobs in various categories were envisaged. As AVM Harjinder Singh stated, "This ever enlarging body of highly skilled technicians are the most valuable by-product of this venture into aircraft manufacture .... this investment in human resources is perhaps the most important aspect of the project."

(In the event, manpower at the Kanpur Division peaked at just over 3,200 in 1982, including 412 officers, most of whom were engineering graduates while a majority of the technicians were ITI-qualified).

After some more test flights, the aircraft was flown to Palam in Delhi where formal ceremonies took place in the presence of Prime Minister Jawaharlal Nehru on November 26, 1961, and it was christened "Subroto" after the first Indian Commander-in-Chief and Chief of Staff of the IAF who had unfortunately died the previous year. Krishna Menon stated, "For us in India, the building of the Avro 748 is not just making an aeroplane but a great landmark in our national and technical progress .... this has instilled greater confidence into our people and it will make a far greater contribution to aviation in India than may now appear".

The Defence Minister conveyed his appreciation to Wing Commander R.H. Chaudhry, Officer Commanding AMD, Squadron Leader Baljit Kapur, AMD's Chief Engineer and all personnel involved in the Avro project, and stated on the occasion that the aircraft was "the precursor of further effort with future versions and models of the Avro itself and of other aircraft."[6] The first aircraft was formally handed over to the Indian Air Force on February 8, 1964, while the first Series 2 aircraft, built from imported knocked-down-assemblies, flew on January 28, 1964, a total of 18 such CKD kits having been delivered to Kanpur from Manchester by November 1966. The first phase orders for the Hawker Siddeley (Avro having been absorbed into the HS Group) covered aircraft for the IAF, most of them fitted out as VIP/executive transports, to serve with the Air HQ Communication Squadron at Palam and with Command Communication Flights, some as navigational and air signal trainers for the Navigation and Signal School

(NSS) at Begumpet and the remaining as multi-engine crew trainers.

The Sino-Indian War in 1962 had a profound impact on a range of issues and areas in India. Krishna Menon was forced to resign in the face of widespread criticism of the defeat and, thus, the Avro project lost its most influential and enthusiastic supporter. This became important in view of a large number of the senior Air Force leadership having been against the IAF undertaking aircraft manufacture since they saw the role of the Air Force purely in terms of air war and its combat support activities which did not include manufacturing of aircraft in the country although the IAF continued to maintain a large number of Base Repair Depots for the overhaul, repair and maintenance of various types of aircraft.

The overall impact was that in June 1964, the Aircraft Manufacturing Depot was incorporated as Aeronautics (India). But from October 1, 1964, with the promulgation of the Aircraft Companies Amalgamation Act, the company was dissolved, to become part of Hindustan Aeronautics Limited (HAL) as its Kanpur Division. In all, over 80 Avro aircraft were manufactured and many continue to be in service with the IAF even today. Orders had been progressively placed for the HS 748s, largely for the IAF and a fair number for Indian Airlines, the latter having also announced its requirement for a freighter version in 1972. However, Indian Airlines, the national domestic carrier, was critical of the aircraft on the grounds of its efficiency as an airliner and doubts remained about its safety and airworthiness and Indian Airlines in particular kept raising objections to the induction of the aircraft into service with it. The highly regarded Scientist Dr. Satish Dhawan, widely regarded as the "Father of India's space programme," was appointed by the government to examine all aspects of the HS-748 and submit his report and recommendations. The Dhawan Committee, in its report submitted to Raj Bahadur, Minister of Tourism and Civil Aviation, concluded that the Avro HS-748 Aircraft in the Indian Airlines fleet "meets the current international standards of airworthiness and safety".

Throughout the 748 programme at HAL, Kanpur, the orders from the IAF for different versions, Indian Airlines, National Remote Sensing Agency, Directorate General of Civil Aviation (DGCA) and Border Security Force kept coming in small batches. This posed a problem of capacity utilisation, especially after the orders for the Avro wound down by the late 1970s. In order to utilise the surplus capacity, HAL transferred a number of projects to Chakeri, including manufacture of the HPT-32 primary trainers in the early 1980s, Aradhra gliders, MiG-drop tanks, and tail-retarder units for bombs. HAL, Kanpur, developed the HMG-1 motorised-glider, based on the Aradhra sail plane earlier manufactured for the National Cadet Corps (NCC) and gliding clubs, but this was not put into production because by 1984, the Kanpur Division was to be transformed for large-scale production of the Dornier 228 family of light transport aircraft.

Licensed Production Preempts Design and Development

Krishna Menon had toyed with the manufacture of light transport aircraft like the DHC Otter (of which two squadrons had been acquired on the eve of the 1962 War). But more than two decades would elapse before a light aircraft began to be manufactured in India, and that too under licence.

In 1974, the government had set up a multi-disciplinary committee under the Director Aero, Dr. Vivek Sinha (later Additional Secretary DR&DO) to not only examine the requirement for such feeder air links, but to identify places to be air-connected, quantify the size, type and number of aircraft required and, finally, determine whether the indigenous aircraft industry was capable of developing and producing such an aircraft in the time and numbers required. Why this sort of task was not assigned to the Indian Air Force (where scientific acumen could be coopted) as the user which had a vital stake in the matter defies logic.

The answers of the Sinha Committee were clear: the country required such regional air links for social, economic and strategic reasons; connecting over 50 points throughout the subcontinent would eventually justify air employment of 18 to 20-seater light transport aircraft; and well over 100 aircraft would be needed. Hindustan Aeronautics Limited had the expertise and resources to undertake this national task. Even as the Design and Development Bureau of HAL, under the direction of S.C. Das, started preliminary design studies for such an aircraft, eventually labelled the HAC-33 in 1976, the domestic carrier, Indian Airlines, nominated their Planning Manager, J.K. Chaudhuri, in 1977, to initiate an examination of third-level air traffic potential; and identify city pairs to be connected, the frequency of operation and the likely type of aircraft that could fulfil the needs. Both reports were positive in their conclusion, and became the springboard for a simultaneous approach towards the objectives of creating a third-level airline and having an indigenous aircraft serve it.

The Ministry of Civil Aviation constituted a number of committees in 1979-80 with virtually the same terms of reference as had earlier been entrusted to Gidwani: the Zaheer Committee, followed by the Braganza Committee, were tasked to make recommendations regarding the nature, type and size of aircraft, to identify the stations, other than the northeastern ones, which should be covered by third-level air services, assess the number of aircraft required to serve the stations and recommend the airfield infrastructure required so that the entire country could be covered in phases over three years. The Braganza Committee submitted its report in late 1980. Clearly, this too, fell short of what the government desired: a larger view had to be taken, bringing in the requirements not only of the proposed third-level airline, but also of the multifarious operators of such category of light transport aircraft in the country and, vitally, the involvement of India's aircraft industry in such a programme.

At the same time, HAL had the HAC-33 (under S.C. Das) under serious consideration. It appears that there were no serious sponsors for the HAL design. It has not been possible to ascertain whether the IAF issued a requirement for such an aircraft knowing that the light aircraft in its inventory (the Caribou and Otter) would be phased out in less than a decade and replacements would be needed. Air HQ was in the best position to make the judgement (in consultation with Army HQ and Naval HQ) to work out the peace-time needs as well as surge requirements in case of a crisis or war. Slowly, but steadily, a number of committees, and many years later, a foreign designed and developed aircraft in the shape of the Dornier 228 was selected and we seem to have been satisfied with "participating" in its production and minor changes required for different operators. Even when the Dornier 338 and its factory was going into bankruptcy, South Block and HAL did not pay any attention to the potential for acquiring the larger aircraft and the rights to the design and further developing and manufacturing it in the country as part of the overall deal. The comfort level of licensed production seems to have weighed heavily with the thinking in South Block!

HAL-Dornier 228

The contract signed between the Government of India and Dornier GmbH of Germany on November 29, 1983, paved the way for India's national aeronautical industry to manufacture a light transport aircraft for a variety of roles. Five years earlier, in May 1978, HAL and Dornier signed a Memorandum, of Understanding to design, develop and manufacture a light transport aircraft incorporating the "wing of new technology" evolved in Germany. Dornier was a highly respected company with roots from the dawn of aviation history and having undertaken at the time, a concept study for a 19-24 seat light transport aircraft on their drawing board. At the same time, HAL had the HAC-33 (under S.C. Das) under serious consideration. It appears that there were no serious sponsors for the HAL design and/or different motives were in action with numerous organisations ranging from the nationalised airlines to South Block and HAL.

A large number of design engineers from HAL led by Wing Commander Inder Chopra (later Chairman of HAL) was nominated for joint studies with the Dornier team led by Reinhold Birrenbach at Friedrichshafen on the Lake of Constance in southern Germany, and at the completion some months later, positive recommendations were framed for the government's consideration. However, it took several years of appraisal, flight evaluation to the farthest limits of performance and intensive commercial and industrial negotiations before the Government of India confirmed, in August 1983, selection of the derivative Dornier 228 as India's choice of light transport aircraft for various operators, including the new regional airline Vayudoot, the IAF, the Navy and Coast Guard plus other operators. The rationale for feeder air links within the vast country was understood and promoted for nearly a decade before Vayudoot, India's regional or third-level airline, came into being in January 1981. Successive Ministers for Civil Aviation had periodically announced that the government was studying the possibility of establishing such air services to link hitherto unconnected points, particularly in the Northeast; that various options as to the kind of air carrier were being examined and that various suitable aircraft types were being evaluated. In fact, it was after the fifth successive committee's report that such an airline took formal shape, assumed a name and began air services, albeit with the Avro shed by Indian Airlines. It was up to the sixth committee to select the most efficient and cost-effective aircraft to match the nation's objectives. Most of the deliberations took place through the Seventies.

In early 1981, the government constituted the Menon Committee, with members nominated from the airlines, Captain Kamini Chadha, Chairman Indian Airlines, Air Force, Air Marshal Kapil Chadha, and industry, J. Bhandari, Chief of Planning, Hindustan Aeronautics Limited and later General Manager, Kanpur Division. The Menon Committee had extensive discussions with potential operators of such light transport aircraft, studied the size and performance parameters and worked out **projected requirements till the end of the century** before drawing up a list of all available aircraft types then existing. Nearly two years of examination, flight evaluation to the farthest limits of performance and intensive commercial and industrial negotiations followed before the Government of India confirmed, in August 1983, selection of the Dornier 228 as India's choice of light transport aircraft for Vayudoot/IAF, Navy and Coast Guard plus other operators. In the process, the design and development of the HAC-33 landed up in the dustbin of history. It does not appear that

Dornier consultancy was ever sought to design and develop an Indian light transport aircraft in the 1970s which would have enabled the country to design and develop a larger (80-100 seat transport aircraft) at a later date.

The Dornier 228 represented a new generation of commuter and utility aircraft, incorporating advanced technology in design and manufacture, and potential for future growth. Conforming to FAR 23 Part 135 Appendix 'A' regulations for commuter operations, the 19-seater Dornier 228-200 series had the twin, and normally incompatible advantages of Short Take-Off and Landing (STOL) performance in hot-and-high conditions as well as high cruise speed and long range, all at unusually low operating costs. This would make the aircraft extremely versatile and cost-effective for Vayudoot which could operate the aircraft with flexibility and reliability from a variety of airfields, including semi-prepared airstrips in difficult terrain. With its operating costs some one-third of those of competitive aircraft, Vayudoot could plan economic returns on new and unknown sectors.

For the defence services, the Dornier 228 provided equal versatility combining excellent field performance with good payload-range and long endurance, apart from the saving in fuel and maintenance costs owing to its rugged design features. HAL's Kanpur Division was selected to manufacture the airframe, including the wing of new technology, and composite materials for its structure while the Garrett TPE331-5 turboprop engines would be built at the Engine Division in Bangalore and accessories and avionics at HAL's Lucknow and Hyderabad Divisions. Indian operators could take advantage of various developmental benefits that an aircraft like the Dornier 228 at the beginning of its career portended.

That the HAL-built Dornier 228 was intended not only to be a fully indigenous aircraft but one on which future transport aircraft designs are based, was evident from the Indian government's comprehensive planning where even raw material for the airframe/accessories and engines was locally sourced. That, plus the programme for export of HAL-built 228s to a large "exclusive marketing territory", was a major step towards fulfilment of the national policy for self-reliance in the aeronautical field not adequately undertaken, since a quarter century later, we see no signs of a transport aircraft of any type on HAL's list of projects, except for the more recent talk of a medium tactical aircraft.

A project management team under the leadership of C.L. Khosla, Additional GM and including B.K. Banerjee, Jain and M.K. Shanmugam from HAL were deputed to the Dornier facilities in the suburbs of Munich, as also the head office and design department at Immenstaad, near Friedrichshafen on the Bodensee (Lake of Constance). The detailed project report included schedules of training, documentation, installation of plant machinery and equipment, receipt of assemblies, and so on, and a German technical supervisory team was established under Helmut Conen, located at Chakeri, where a German Guest House was built at the HAL township. The facilities at HAL's Kanpur Division clearly had to be augmented and a brand new plant was designed and built across the apron, opposite the original hangars and steel hangar which was temporarily used for assembling the first Dornier 228s which were flown in by special 'Guppy' freighters from Oberpfaffenhofen to Chakeri. The new final assembly hangar, NC machine shops and autoclave centres (considerable structure of the aircraft is of composite material) plus paint shops were ready by 1985-86 and began work on Phase IV (or raw material) aircraft immediately. There were many spin-offs from the new technology introduced into HAL with the Chakeri factory producing wings for the Jaguar strike fighter, while the HPT-32 basic trainer was to benefit from the 228's wing of new technology design.

Initial deliveries of the Dornier 228s, built at the manufacturer's plant at Oberpfaffenhofen, south of Munich, took place ceremoniously in November 1984, the first three aircraft to the Indian regional airline, Vayudoot, and these were followed by aircraft destined for the Indian Coast Guard, National Airports Authority (NAA), Oil and Natural Gas Commission and Indian Navy. Alongside, Dornier supplied the Dornier 228s in kit form for assembly by HAL for Vayudoot, the Coast Guard, NAA and Indian Air Force.

As with other transfer-of-technology programmes, licensed manufacture of the Dornier 228 was in progressive steps, beginning with Phase Zero (supply of a minimum number of "flyaways" directly from the licensors), then CKD-kits sent to the licensee under Phase I (six aircraft), followed by Phases II and III (ten aircraft each as sub-assemblies and detailed parts). Phase IV, or the raw material stage was to begin for 27 aircraft onwards and HAL was confident that it would achieve its target of 150 aircraft to be built for both the Indian and export markets. With the original designers and manufacturers Dornier Lufthart GmbH changing their corporate strategy to concentrate on regional jet airlines from the mid-1990s, HAL was to become the sole manufacturer of the Dornier 228 light transport aircraft, with worldwide export rights.

The first HAL-built Dornier 228 light transport aircraft had its maiden flight on January 31, 1986, flown by HAL's Chief Test Pilot, Wing Commander B.K. Dhiman, the second, third, fourth and fifth HAL-built Dornier 228s following swiftly with their first flights on February 21, March 5, March 13 and,

March 20 respectively. On March 22, 1986, the first of five HAL-built Dornier 228 light transport aircraft were handed over at Chakeri airfield, Kanpur, to Vayudoot, the regional airline which earlier had taken over the Avro from Indian Airlines.

The Helicopters of HAL

HAL's involvement with rotary-wing aircraft dates back to June 1962 when, to meet the Indian Air Force's requirement for light helicopters, the Government of India signed a licence agreement with Sud-Aviation of France (consequently renamed SNIAS or Aerospatiale and now part of Eurocopter), as also Turbomeca for the production of its Artouste power plant. The first helicopter type to be built at HAL, Bangalore, was the Alouette III, later named Chetak, with firm orders having been placed in January 1965, and the "raw material" production phase beginning in 1969-70. The Alouette II, with the dynamics including the power plant of the Alouette III was specifically developed to meet the Indian Army's stringent requirement and was christened Lama by the French (and Cheetah by the Indians). The SA-315B licence-agreement was signed in September 1970. The first Cheetah manufactured from raw materials was delivered in 1976-77. In the initial stages of helicopter manufacturing, except for the assembly departments, all other shops were common with those of the Aircraft Division. Consequent to the reorganisation of the Bangalore Complex, a separate division was evolved for the manufacture of helicopters, established in July 1970 and the new buildings of the Helicopter Division inaugurated by the then President of India, V.V. Giri on July 17, 1974.

HAL's Helicopter Division produced hundreds of Chetak and Cheetah helicopters for the Indian Air Force, Navy, Army and Coast Guard as also for a number of civilian customers, including state governments over the next twenty years, while a score or more were exported. More than 250 Chetaks/Cheetahs have also been overhauled by the division at Bangalore. The Helicopter Division, to which is adjoined the Helicopter Design Bureau (now Rotary Wing R&D Centre) and Advanced Light Helicopter (ALH) prototype hangars, has 42,000 sq. m of factory buildings in which the manufacturing, assembly and testing facilities are established. The division employs 1,100 persons, including engineers, and is set to expand with the envisaged series production of the ALH.

Major servicing of more than 200 helicopters and the overhaul of rotables are also undertaken at the Helicopter Division, which is also the maintenance agency for some civil operators, and carries out the T1/T2 inspection on schedule. Category 'B' repairs have also been carried out on more than 100 helicopters, plus more than 150 modifications for the Chetak and 87 modifications for the Cheetah have been undertaken. The Helicopter Division has equipped naval Chetaks for the match role as well as for the scientific expeditions to Antarctica.

Aerospatiale/HAL Alouette (Chetak)

By the late 1950s, it was obvious that the Indian armed forces would need far greater numbers of rotorcraft than the handful of Bell 47Gs and Sikorsky S-55s could fulfil. The choice of the light utility helicopter fell on the French Alouette III and on June 4, 1962, the Government of India signed a licensed-agreement with Sud-Aviation and Turbomeca for production by HAL of the SA-316B Alouette III helicopter and its Artouste IIIB turbine of 450 shp. Teams sent to France for pre-planning work envisaged a gradual build-up of manufacturing capacity at HAL, Bangalore, with the first batch to be assembled from imported major assemblies, sub-assemblies, and detail parts. To meet the lAF's urgent requirement for helicopters, some Alouette Ills were directly imported even as preparations were afoot at Bangalore for the progressive manufacture of a large number of Alouette IIIs ordered by the IAF in January and June 1965. In fact, the first HAL-assembled helicopter flew on June 11, 1965.

Production of the Alouette III till 1968 was confined to major assembly work although manufacture of smaller components had begun and, gradually, production from raw materials began, the first Alouette III (now named the Chetak) making its maiden flight at Bangalore on June 21, 1969, by which time the IAF had ordered another batch and the Navy had placed orders for a dozen such helicopters. The Engine Division was gearing up to match the production of the Artouste IIIB turbine engine, and eight different types of aluminium and magnesium alloys began to be locally produced. An armed version for the Air Force, equipped with four AS-11B anti-tank wire-guided missiles was also developed by 1976-77 and some 40 Chetaks were eventually built for use by three such Helicopter Units. The first Coast Guard orders were placed in 1979. Orders continued to be placed and the total number of Chetaks finally produced by HAL's Helicopter Division came to well over 300.

Aerospatiale/HAL SA-315B Lama (Cheetah)

Design and development of the SA 315B was initiated by Aerospatiale late in 1968, primarily to meet a requirement announced by the Indian armed forces for a lightweight multi-role helicopter capable of effective operations in the high, mountains. During demonstration flights in the Himalayas in 1969, the SA 315B, carrying a crew of two and 308 Ib (140 kg) of fuel, made the highest landings and take-offs ever recorded, from a height of 24,600 ft (7,500 m.). In September 1970, an agreement was signed with the French company for manufacture of the SA-315B under licence at HAL, Bangalore. The first 20 were SA-315Bs to be produced from sub-assemblies obtained from France and the other 80 were to be subsequently manufactured at HAL's new helicopter factory then being established at Bangalore. The first HAL-assembled helicopter (Z 1431) initially flew on October 6, 1972, and was handed over for trials with the IAF at Bangalore on December 14, being cleared for service in early 1973. A first batch of six Lamas had been accepted by the Indian Air Force/Army by late 1973.

The SA-315B, soon named the Cheetah in IAF service, were utilised for a variety of roles, including liaison, rescue, training, ambulance or observation. Rethinking on the employment of fixed-wing aircraft in mountain terrain and the fact that rotary-wing aircraft have greater versatility with their Vertical Take-off and Landing (VTOL)/hovering capabilities led the Cheetah into supplanting the Krishaks for the Air OP (Air Observation Post) role, and when the AOP force was transferred to the Indian Army in November 1986, the majority of helicopters were Cheetahs. The Indian Army has utilised the Cheetah most effectively in the ultra-high altitude areas of northeast Kashmir, the light helicopter providing the virtual lifeline for troops, manning the pickets in the high mountains overlooking the Siachen Glacier of Ladakh and in the Karakorams. Additional orders for the Cheetah were placed on HAL and by 1999, well over 200 such helicopters had been produced. An armed version, the Lancer, has been evolved by HAL from the Cheetah for light attack tasks, its utility even more vital since the Kargil operations in the summer of 1999.

INDIGENOUS DESIGN AND DEVELOPMENT

NAL's Saras

Curiously, the only fixed-wing aircraft in India for which indigenous design and development has been undertaken since the HF-24 (initiated in 1956) and the LCA in 1987, is the Saras light transport aircraft. This interestingly has been undertaken by the National Aerospace Laboratories (NAL, earlier called the National Aeronautics Laboratory) established for basic research into aerodynamics, etc under the CSIR (Council for Scientific and Industrial Research) under the Ministry of Science and Technology. NAL had successfully designed and constructed a training (non-aerobatic) aircraft called Hansa for the flying clubs and private flying before undertaking the Saras project.

The Saras project began in 1991 as a collaborative project with the Russian company Myasishchev (which had a similar project of its own) but financial troubles led the Russians to drop out. US sanctions, enhanced after 1998, led to a series of delays. The first Saras PT-1 (Prototype 1) successfully completed its first flight at Bangalore on May 29, 2004. The aircraft was displayed in a flying demonstration in Aero India 2007 at Yelahanka near Bangalore. But the aircraft suffered from the same problem that affected almost all HAL aircraft: increase of weight which in the case of the Saras was almost 25 percent of the planned empty weight, leaving the aircraft underpowered. This has been sought to be solved by reducing the extra weight by 500 kg and using a more powerful engine, the 1,200 hp engine instead of the 850hp Pratt and Whitney engine used in Saras PT-1. The second prototype flew on April 20, 2007. The total sanctioned project cost has been quoted at Rs. 139 crore (US$ 30 million).

NAL is now planning a more ambitious project in design and development of a larger transport aircraft with a capacity of 80-odd seats.

HAL's MTA

At the same time, HAL had signed a $700 million collaboration agreement in December 2006 for joint design, development and sales for a Multi-role Transport Aircraft (MTA). The partner from the Russian side was the United Aircraft Corporation & Rosoboronexport for the 50/50 joint venture. The twin-engine 60-65 ton maximum all-up take-off weight aircraft is planned to have a payload of 15-20 tons (thus, providing the alternative for the An-12 which had served the IAF well for nearly four decades). This would obviate the need to seek a Western aircraft in this class and range which is critical where heavy lift is not required and, thus, would meet the needs of the IAF and the Russian Air Force. The Ilyushin Design Bureau of Russia would design the aircraft and Irkut Corporation would develop it, while the series production would be taken up by the transport aircraft division of HAL at Kanpur.[7] Irkut is the major investor (40 percent of the project expenses) and will be the main coordinator from the Russian side. The project has the approval of both governments.

The MTA, with a planned manufacture of 145 aircraft for Russia and India of which around 45 are likely to be ordered by the IAF in the first instance (which may go up to over 100 aircraft), is planned to have state-of-the-art features such as fly-by-wire controls, full authority digital engine, modern avionics and glass cockpit. The total development costs is expected to be around US$ 600 million (approximately Rs. 2,900 crore) equally shared by the two sides. The plan is to ultimately manufacture 205 aircraft, with 50-50 work share between the two partners. A joint venture company is being established with its headquarters at Bangalore to manage the project, with both sides having equal shares.

ALH: Advanced Light Helicopter

HAL's Helicopter Design Bureau began the indigenous design of an Advanced Light Helicopter (ALH) and the programme was first announced in November 1984. The initiation, progress and successful results of this programme stand out as a major (and perhaps the only one, except for a couple of trainers) success story of HAL, no doubt, because the Helicopter Design Bureau (integrated with the Helicopter Production Division) is perhaps the only one that has survived the dissipation of the main design bureau and this carries an obvious lesson for the future; and this is undoubtedly a major factor in the success of the complete venture of design, development and production of the first Indian helicopter. The ALH, named the Dhruv (a Sanskrit word meaning Polaris star), was designed with assistance from the German company, MBB (Messerschmitt-Bolkow-Blom) which was named as the design consultant. The civil prototype first flew ten years later on August 23, 1992, at Bangalore, followed by a second civil aircraft, and then by one with Army specifications, to be followed by a navalised version.

There were inevitable problems that impact such programmes in a developing country's first attempt at design and development of an aircraft. Sanctions after the 1998 nuclear tests aggravated them due to the embargo on the US engine (Allied Signal, later Honeywell CTS800) originally planned for the helicopter. The HF-24 story was almost going to be replayed. But then two Turbomeca TM 333-2B2 turboshaft engines (1,000 hp) each were installed and an agreement

signed with Turbomeca to jointly develop a more powerful
engine, to be named Shakti and the first test flight with the
new engines took place on August 16, 2007.[8] The more recent
versions of the ALH are all powered by the Shakti engines and
are equipped with state-of-the-art carbon-fibre construction,
fitted with a SFIM four-axis automatic flight control system,
GPS and Doppler navigation system, etc.

Deliveries of the LCA to the users began in 2002 and 45
helicopters were delivered to the three Indian armed forces
by 2007. Its unit cost is believed to be around Rs. 40 crore
(US$ 9.08 million).[9] The helicopter is capable of flying at
very high altitudes, recording a performance of landing at
the Siachen region at an altitude of 27,500 ft in October
2007. A further order for 166 helicopters was placed after
the demonstration mostly to meet the requirements of the
IAF and Indian Army at high altitudes. The helicopters
have also been ordered by civilian security agencies and the
National Disaster Management Authority. With a unit cost
of at least 15-30 percent lower than its rivals, the Dhruv,
built to international design standards stipulated by the
US FAR (Federal Acquisition Regulations) and US Military
Specifications as a unique multi-role, state-of-the-art, cost-
effective helicopter in the 4-5 ton class is well positioned
for exports. At least 24 helicopters have been exported to
nine countries, this being the most significant arms export by
India. Till 2010, there have been four accidents of Dhruv, two
attributed to pilot error and two due to technical failure (one
for loss of power and the other for a fault in the tail rotor
blades). Although the ALH can carry 8 anti-tank missiles or
4 air-to-air missiles, HAL has an ongoing programme for an
attack helicopter.

HAL Light Combat Helicopter

In 2006, HAL announced plans for the design and manufacture of a Light Combat Helicopter (LCH) for the Indian Air Force and Indian Army on the basic airframe of the ALH Dhruv with a weight of 5.5 tons and the maximum speed of 25 kmph, higher than that of the Dhruv. The government sanctioned US$24 million for the design, development and production of two LCH prototypes by 2008 and HAL planned to deliver the attack helicopter for induction in service by 2012. Based on the confidence of the ALH Dhruv, HAL has firm orders to deliver 65 LCH to the Indian Air Force and 114 to the Indian Army.

The maiden flight of the LCH took place on March 29, 2010, a few months later than planned, followed by a second flight on April 28, 2010. According to Ashok Naik, Chairman HAL, the LCH project has been undertaken with an outlay of Rs. 376 crore, of which, 10 per cent has been borne by the public sector company.[10] "The LCH is designed to meet the operational needs of the IAF and is equipped with mission sensors. Among its multiple roles are attacking slow moving aerial targets, destruction of enemy air defences operations, escort to special heliborne operations and offensive employment in urban warfare counter-surface operations," stated the Chairman HAL.[11]

The ALH Dhruv derivative proves that the **HAL design bureau, where it has functioned as it should have, has produced outstanding results like the HF-24, HJT-16, Dhruv ALH and now the LCH. The last case also demonstrates the critical importance of follow-on design and incremental design and development.** Hence, the weaknesses of the Indian aircraft industry have to be looked for elsewhere.

OUTRIGHT PURCHASE FROM ABROAD

The list of transport aircraft indicated above in this chapter clearly indicates that almost all transport aircraft have been imported and licensed production, initiated in the case of the Avro by the IAF at the Aircraft Manufacturing Depot (later taken over by HAL) commenced in 1959 and the Dornier 228 manufacture started three decades later. The imported transport aircraft since independence are listed below:

Table 6.2

Type	Quantity	Method of Acquisition
Pre-1962:		
Dakota C-47/DC-3	100 plus	Mostly reconstructed from WWII old/damaged stocks
Packet C-119G	79	Direct purchase from USA
DHC Caribou	18	Direct purchase from Canada
DHC Otter	21	Direct purchase from Canada
Post-1962:		
An-12B	41	Direct purchase from USSR
IL-14	24	Direct purchase from USSR
IL-76/78	48 app	Direct purchase from USSR/ FSU
An-32	98	Direct purchase from USSR

Of these, two cases are worth recording. One deals with the Packet C-119G medium lift transport useful for air-dropping supplies. However, it did not have the power to safely cross over the mountain peaks in Ladakh. It was, therefore, decided to install a jet engine on top of the fuselage to provide it significantly more power to operate at higher altitudes. The Bristol Orpheus-3 installed in the HF-24 was selected for this purpose and the engine installed on top of the fuselage. With this configuration, Squadron Leader (later Air Marshal) C.S.

Raje landed and inaugurated regular operations at the world's highest airfield (over 16,700 ft.), Daulat Beg Oldi, near the Karakoram Pass in Ladakh in 1962.

The second comprises the development of the An-32. The IAF was looking for one aircraft instead of a conglomerate collection of transport aircraft acquired under pressing circumstances with a rapidly increasing demand for air supply. Some of the pressure for air supply was taken over by helicopters. Meanwhile, the Packet aircraft was getting close to its useful design life. Hence, Air HQ decided in the mid-1970s to seek an aircraft from the Soviet Union for medium tactical airlift. The nearest aircraft suitable for this task was the An-26; but it did not have sufficient power and operational ceiling to operate in the Himalayas. And the requirement was to have an aircraft which would be capable of "hot and high" capabilities. It was, therefore, decided that the An-12 engine, for which overhaul facilities existed in India, could be fitted on the An-26; and that, after some delay by the Soviets in carrying out the modification, resulted in the An-32 which was inducted into service in the early 1980s.

SOME TRENDS FOR THE FUTURE

After some hiccups in the early 1990s when the Indian government liberalised the economic and aviation policies, civil aviation in India has been growing at a fairly fast rate, riding over the more recent global economic meltdown with its growth still on track. At present, it is one of the fastest growing aviation industries in the world. Private airlines today account for nearly 75 percent share of the domestic aviation market. In 2008, the year when the global economic meltdown was reaching its peak, the Indian civil aviation market grew at a Compound Annual Growth Rate (CAGR) of 18 per cent and was worth US$ 5.6 billion in that year. Domestic airlines flew 3.67 million passengers in August 2009 as compared 2.92 million in the corresponding month the previous year. By 2020, Indian airports are expected to handle more than 100 million passengers, including 60 million domestic passengers and around 3.4 million tonnes of cargo per annum. The government plans to invest US$ 9 billion to modernise existing airports and is planning to develop nearly 300 unused airstrips.

According to the India Brand Equity Foundation (IBEF), the industry witnessed an annual growth of 12.8 per cent over the five-year period ending 2009 in the international cargo handled at all airports in India. The tourist charter flights have increased dramatically. Boeing (and Airbus) estimate that India would acquire around 1,100 transport aircraft in the coming ten years. It is very likely that a large number of these may be acquired on lease and charter by private airlines, but the potential for the air transport industry is very obvious. One has only to look at Brazil with its regional transport aircraft and the Chinese industry to see where we are lagging in spite of an aircraft industry established a little over seven decades ago.

The basic problem in the transport sector of the aircraft industry has been that, firstly, civil aviation policies and requirements are handled by the Ministry of Civil Aviation, often without coordination with the Defence Ministry that lays down the policy for military transport aircraft/helicopters, airfields and aviation infrastructure. This has been very obvious in the government policy on offsets and maintenance, repair and overhaul. Wiser men had strongly argued for the establishment of an Aeronautics Commission decades ago exactly for the purpose of coordinating and synergising the efforts of various agencies and institutions that affect aeronautics and aviation activities.

Notes

1. Atma Ram, "Mechanics of Self-Reliance," NIF 1972-73, Annual Number, pp. 77-80, emphasis in original, cited by Baldev Nayar, *India's Quest for Technological Independence: Policy Foundations and Policy* Change, Vol. I (New Delhi: Lancer Publishers, 1983), p. 494.

2. M.R. Dhekney, *Air Transport in India (Growth and Problems)* (Bombay: Vora & Co., 1953), Appendix A, p. 241

3. Air Commodore A.L. Saigal, *Birth of an Air Force; The Memoirs of Air Vice Marshal Harjinder Singh* (New Delhi: Palit & Palit Publishers, 1977), p. 263.

4. Ibid., p. 262

5. This was interesting since it gave the country an opportunity to acquire weapon systems of the state-of-the-art technology and systems at that time. Compared to this, the IAF was unwilling to look at the Russian MiG-AT for the AJT role since it was "still under development" in the late 1980s and kept pressing for a single vendor supplied British Aerospace Hawk trainer which was ultimately contracted for in 2004.

6. Pushpinder Singh, *Diamonds in the Sky, Sixty Years of HAL 1940-2001* (New Delhi: Society for Aerospace Studies, 2001), p. 77.

7. See http://www.defenseindustrydaily.com/hal-and-irkuts-joint-tactical-tr

8. "Shakti-Powered ALH to Fly on August 1" in *The Hindu*, at http://hindu.com/2007/07/19/stories/2007071950150900.com retrieved August 31, 2010.

9. Huma Siddiqui, "HAL in a Dhruv Ride in LatAm," *The Indian Express*, July 15, 2008.

10. "Light Combat Helicopter Dedicated to Nation," *The Hindu*, May 23, 2010.

11. "First India-Built Light Combat Helicopter Unveiled," *Hindustan Times*, May 23, 2010.

12. Report on "Aviation" by IBEF (India Brand Equity Foundation), at http://www.ibef.org, accessed on February 9, 2010.

7

Rebuilding Self-Reliance
Opportunities, Options and Prospects

The fact of the matter is that the aircraft industry is a high science, high-technology (and high-cost) industry. It is driven by long-term perspectives of future requirements, and tends to have long gestation periods for developing successful R&D and specific technologies in anticipation of potential future requirements. If the Air Force conceives a threat scenario that would develop ten years from now, the technologies that are required to develop a suitable aircraft must be already available, when the Air Force issues its Air Staff Requirement (ASR).

— Dr. S. R. Valluri, former Director NAL[1]

Research, design and development, manufacture and inspection are all integrated and inter-related activities. *They must, therefore, be organisationally unified to obtain optimum results.*

— Major General B.D. Kapur[2]

India's economic growth rate at an average of 8 percent over the past decade, and the trend of its continuing growth at or above such levels, clearly creates an unprecedented opportunity to build its aerospace industry in the coming years. Though the country has come a long way from what was described in Chapters 1 and 2, the deficit in the aircraft industry still is very much larger than what was possible primarily because of the collapse of the three-strand self-reliance model which started immediately after independence. This had been essentially caused by relying increasingly on licensed manufacturing without any steps to continue the nascent design and development capabilities and raise them to higher levels where by now we should have been in a position to be an equal partner in joint design and development of aircraft at the minimum, preferably able to design and develop a range of aircraft types ourselves. The critical needs have been training aircraft at all three stages of training (primary, intermediate and lead-in-fighter trainers), combat aircraft and other types.

When one looks at the issues objectively in a historical context, one is surprised at the fact that while HAL set about designing a multi-role combat aircraft with supersonic capabilities, the HF-24 Marut — no doubt an ambitious goal at that time — as early as the mid-1950s, it took the country over three decades to get down to design and develop the next combat aircraft, the LCA, for the battlefield air superiority and strike role. And to undertake this task, HAL was considered incapable or unwilling, steeped as it was in the four decades of the comfort of licensed manufacture which had the advantage of no questions being asked about fulfilling the ASR specifications, time and cost overruns, etc. And there was a mark up percentage on the sale price to the IAF as the icing on the licensed production cake. The institutional structures were hardly conducive to technology development for building design and development capabilities.

During the three decades that elapsed between the start of the design process for the HF-24 and the LCA (which, like the other licensed manufactured aircraft, does not carry the HAL's prefix since it did not design it), aviation technology had advanced exponentially, making it all the more difficult to harness it indigenously. Progressive expansion of technology denial regimes and sanctions further created serious handicaps in the process of technology access from even friendly countries. No steps appear to have been taken to initiate a joint venture to design and develop any aircraft of any type with the Soviet Union during the decades the relationship was flowering and the USSR possessed enormous design capacity and capabilities for high-end aerospace systems. Even when the USSR disintegrated in end-1991 and their military industry leaders were keen to collaborate with India, no steps were taken to tie up at least in some selected areas. Ultimately, New Delhi provided financial assistance four years after the Soviet disintegration for the development of the Sukhoi Su-30 to Su-30MKI standard.

It may be useful here to look briefly at the lessons we should/ can draw from the past. But before that, it may be helpful to outline the broad parameters of the aircraft industry in Russia (from where we have been buying our aircraft for the past half century) and China (which has built up its aircraft industry from a very low level to a foremost industry now) to see if there are any lessons that may be of use to us.

Soviet/Russian Defence Industry

Here, it may be useful to look at the Russian and Chinese approach to the basic issue of the nature of relationship between research institutions, design bureaus and production agencies. There is no doubt that the Soviet Union invested enormous resources in its arms production, especially during the Cold War, when sheer numbers rather than high-technology arms were deployed. But here what we wish to see are the more limited aspects of their policy and organisation for aircraft design, development and production. Russia/the Soviet Union had acquired enormous experience in aircraft design, development and production from the early years after manned flight started. During the chaotic year of 1917, the aviation industry produced 1,099 aircraft and 374 engines. The following figures at different periods till the early years of World War II indicate the scale at which the Russian aviation industry was functioning:[3]

	Table 7.1
Years	Aircraft Production
1918-1927	20,847
1929-1939	45,499 (including 29,435 military aircraft)
1939-1941	13,852 (older models)
1942 expansion	25,436 aircraft, 38,002 engines

At the core of the above performance was the nationalisation of aircraft factories on June 28, 1918, and the decision taken in 1921 to build a strong military air arm. Accordingly, the 1928 plan for the Soviet aviation industry was "to rid itself of foreign dependence."[4] By 1939, about 37 airframe, engine and components plants are believed to have existed in the Soviet Union. World War II only multiplied this manifold. The difference between the Russian/Soviet approach and that of post-independence India was in the large national resources allocated by Moscow to the aviation industry compared to what New Delhi was able or willing to do; **and even more important, Russian integration of design, development and production functions under one agency for different aircraft**.

At the same time, the Soviet Union/Russia created a system of *competitive design* that could be initiated by the various experimental design bureaus called OKB (*opytniye konstruk-torskiye byura*) while the government maintained the right to select what it wanted to be taken forward for production. This resulted in a number of designs and even prototypes produced that did not lead to production. Inevitably, the designers became the dominant leaders at the head each of a number of aircraft factories, and even aircraft came to be known under the name of the designer.[5] In other words, a number of integrated design and manufacturing organisational structures prospered in various competitive design bureaus heading the system in the aviation industry.

After World War II, a Ministry of Aviation Industry was established to coordinate the efforts of various OKBs and carry out the selection of the design to be produced in the numbers required (from the larger numbers designed and even produced to prototype stage by the OKBs), thus, also creating domestic competition among them. For example, between 1938-40, "OKBs projected, built, and tested 115 new aircraft and 83 modified models. Of these, 31 new aircraft and 36 modifications reached state acceptance trials, but only 20 of these were approved for serial production."[6] The ministry continued to be headed by professional scientists/ designers and the Minister normally stayed in his job for many years (the last Soviet Minister of Aviation Industry was Dr. A.S. Systov during 1985-91).[7] Compared to this, with some notable exceptions, the tenure of the Secretary, Defence Production (who controls all defence public sector enterprises) in office, has averaged around 9 months in India!

Nearly 80 percent of the German aircraft production facilities fell into Soviet hands after World War II ended in Europe. But, "All these items were carefully collected, evaluated, tested and flown by the Soviets, but closer examination showed that most of the technological left-overs from the frantic high-technology of the Third Reich had little value for the Soviets."[8] Another view holds that the Soviets greatly benefited by the American lend-lease arrangements in their aircraft industry. It would be obvious that they gained extensively in copying the design and technology of the relatively advanced technology American aircraft. But as far as numbers are concerned, only 18,303 aircraft constituting a mere 11.9 percent of the aircraft produced in the Soviet Union during World War II came through the lend-lease route. The Soviet Union produced a total of 142,775 aircraft (and 208,875 engines), all of them being equal or superior to the German designs. Its capacity may be judged by the fact that during 1944 alone the Soviet Union produced 33,205 aircraft (of which 82.5 percent were combat aircraft).[9]

The Kremlin laid down a basic strategy of "Catch up with the West" which then focussed on four areas:[10]

1. Aircraft for air defence purposes.
2. Tactical aircraft (after World War II).
3. Modern bomber fleet (which started to grow rapidly after 1950).
4. Modern transport fleet.

The enormous focus on the aircraft industry showed robust results although there was some disruption and drop in production when all aircraft industrial facilities were shifted east of the Urals before the German offensive in World War II. Much of the industry was located close to the sources of raw material to cut the transportation costs and time. The first really successful jet fighter was the MiG-15 with a production run of 15,000 fighters, a large number of which were transferred to the PRC (People's Republic of China under the Communist regime) which tangled with the American F-84 and later F-86s where it performed pretty well against the USAF. The main characteristics of the Soviet aircraft industry were based on the following principles:

•   The designers were the main authority for the management of the defence industry in terms of design and development while the government retained the decisions for selecting the final and mostly demonstrated design capabilities. During their heyday, the design bureaus came up with competitive designs and aircraft (like the MiG-29 Fulcrum and Su-27 Flanker).

- Great decentralisation in aircraft design and development under the OKB which would exercise control over the production facilities and factories.[11] The types of aircraft were named after the designer. For example, the famous MiG series were designed by designers Mikoyan and Guryevich and built in factories under their control.[12] Compared to this, the design bureau of HAL had almost dissipated by the 1980s.

- All combat aircraft were designed and built to operate in the primitive operating conditions and severe winter weather found in many parts of the Soviet Union (hence, there was a heating system in the MiG-21 cockpit but no fresh air blower, leave alone air-conditioning!)

- Aircraft were designed to use limited resources efficiently, and were easy to maintain,

- The OKB generally followed an incremental approach to aircraft design and development instead of the technological "leapfrog". For example, the MiG-21 has undergone improvements through 23 variants, and the Su27/30 is well on its way to future development of modified models. This reduced the risks and costs of aircraft design and development, with enhanced maintainability and sustainability. The cockpit layout and sub-systems of the MiG-21 of all models and the MiG-15/17/19/21/25 have a strong similarities, thus, providing easy transition of pilots to later models.

- The leading aircraft designers were national and even

international celebrities, and the engineers and technicians were an elite in an industry that enjoyed among the highest national priorities during the Cold War.[13]

One more fact needs to be noted. The massive Soviet aircraft industry provided great support to China in virtually creating a brand new air force and support aircraft industry by the time the Communists were coming to power in Beijing in 1949. The technological levels may be judged by the fact that when the Chinese Air Force intervened in the Korean War in 1950, its MiG-15 was suddenly found to be superior to the US F-84 and World War II Mustang fighters. It was only when the US was able to induct the newly designed F-86 Sabres that some sort of equivalence began to operate. While Soviet support to the Chinese aircraft industry dried up after 1954 when the Soviets refused to provide further assistance in China's nuclear weapons programme, China continued to make efforts to improve its aircraft performance through some reverse engineering and some access to Western technology. Its next major breakthrough came after the Soviet Union broke up and Beijing, with enough hard currency assets, was able to import and otherwise access Russian high-technology aircraft (like the Su-27 and Su-30MKK), besides systems like the S-300 for surface-to-air defence.

China's Defence Industry and Technology Acquisition

As noted above, the Soviet Union provided enormous assistance in setting up China's huge military industrial complexes to manufacture all and every type of weapon system, including the design and manufacture of nuclear weapons and ballistic missiles. This led to a situation where *China had no need to cultivate a strong scientific talent capable of designing and engineering the next generation of weapon systems, machine tools, instrumentation or control equipment.* If the Chinese had been on their own from the beginning, they might have been forced to develop an indigenous capability. This is also what happened to India after 1964, except that successive follow-on licensed produced weapons eroded the incentive to design and develop indigenous weapon systems to such a degree that the HAL design bureau had atrophied by the time the IAF needed the AJT and LCA. An ad-hoc separate entity for the design of the LCA in the shape of the Aeronautical Development Agency (ADA) was established with scientists and engineers from various divisions of HAL and a few from other aeronautics related research institutions like NAL and ADE. But placing it under the DRDO as a stand-alone entity broke the integrity of research, design and production of aircraft.

Very soon after the Korean War, tensions in relations between the two Communist giants started to impinge on the defence industry. The Soviets stopped cooperation on the nuclear front and this aggravated the tensions even more. China's access to military technology became circumscribed. It had no other sources of technology access. By the end of the 1950s, the relationship between the Soviet Union and PRC was near breaking point and the final break coincided with the Sino-Indian War in the autumn of 1962. This resulted in a near complete break in the relationship. One effect was that China's technological and defence industrial acumen and capability was frozen at the levels of equipment supplied by the Soviet Union a decade earlier.

Chinese scientists kept trying to undertake reverse engineering and improvements to the original systems supplied by the Soviet Union along with licensed manufacturing capabilities. But the success in improving the quality of weapon systems was marginal at best. China compensated for the increasing obsolescence with increasing production and expanding its military forces. After the Sino-Soviet War in 1969 which put a seal on bilateral relations between the two countries, the United States opened up relations with China. This raised expectations in Beijing that Western technology would now be available — an expectation that was completely shattered by the Tiananmen incident in June 1989 and the resulting sanctions by the US and its allies. It would take the Soviet disintegration and the consequent economic, social and political crises for the relationship to be reestablished, especially in terms of military-technical cooperation. But we are going far ahead of our narrative.

From the very beginning, Mao Zedong's vision of science and technology was somewhat confused. It is not surprising that during the Great Leap Forward in 1958-60, he emphasised technological development through mass participation and greater authority to the Party cadres in the process. During the Great Proletariat Cultural Revolution in the late 1960s, he imposed his social and political criteria on technology and economic activities in the country; and his aim to exclude scientists from the Cultural Revolution failed to translate into practice. The political campaigns demoralised and decimated several generations of scientists (the majority of whom had been trained in the USSR). Most academic, professional and scientific research was stopped as scientists and engineers along with writers and historians were reeducated and sent for "thought reforms" to the countryside and factories.[14] China's sad state of defence capabilities across the board was obvious during its failure to coerce Vietnam during the 1979 Sino-Vietnam border war. It was estimated that the damage to the country's modest science and technology infrastructure and education by the Cultural Revolution would take years to repair. This, in turn, gave Deng Xiaoping the opportunity and freedom to institute the famous four modernisations which were premised on priority to economic reforms and growth to provide the financial resources for military modernisation. But serious debates on the advantages and risks of access to Western science and technology and the potential of Western values also coming in with the technology access continued till the 1989 incidents blocked the prospects of Western technology transfer.

But the important point to note is that China carried out a series of reforms as part of the modernisation process. Deng Xiaoping linked development of science and technology to the new economic structures that were being created during the first decade of modernisation so that they both would become interdependent. Its most significant step was the defence industry being tasked to also produce goods for the civil market. Military industrial reforms in most countries took place through direct intervention aimed at targeting certain areas for technology generation by means of funding programmes and national research laboratories or through "indirect" means aimed at market modifications that encourage innovation. The result of the Chinese reforms was that within a few years, 50 percent of the output in military industry was in consumer goods. Two other points deserve careful attention. First, "during the 1949-1983 period, China tried to separate defence-related research from that of actual weapon production."[15] Second, China opted for incremental progress in science and technology and weapon designs rather than quantum leaps, thus, lowering the risks and costs of technology acquisition.

According to Tony Saich, the reformers concluded that the centralised system had shown its value in mobilising scarce resources (a significant quantity provided by the production of consumer items for sale in the civil market) to focus on designated problems, but its "inability to provide consistent linkage between research and production sectors was conspicuous. Centralisation had not solved the coordination of work within the research sector."[16] The Party identified the "inability to turn research results into production as the key problem in the post-Mao era" because the vertical structures of the science and technology system with *R&D institutes were responsible to the higher authorities in their own command structures and not developing horizontal links with society and individual production units.* The survey, covering 3,500 scientific institutes throughout the country in 1984, disclosed that "fewer than 10 percent of what the state terms "scientific achievement" had been applied to production."[17] Hence, according to Tony Saich:[18]

> ...**the major organisational problem within the Science and Technology system has been lack of linkage across vertical structures, particularly between the research and production sectors.** Insufficient innovation takes place in industry to bring about the necessary technological advance, and it is difficult to transfer to the production sector the innovation that takes place in the research laboratories. The relative autonomous and isolated situation of the research sector is a problem in most countries, but it is particularly acute in developing countries. Research must be properly integrated with the broader socio-economic structure for optimal use to be made of scientific discovery and technical development." (Emphasis added.)

As Saich has written, the separation of R&D and production is not unique to China. But in India, this seems to have been institutionalised. For example, the charter and mission of the DRDO placed on its website says:[19]

Defence Research & Development Organisation (DRDO) works under Department of Defence Research and Development of Ministry of Defence. DRDO is dedicatedly working towards enhancing self-reliance in Defence Systems and undertakes design & development *leading to production* of world class weapon systems and equipment in accordance with the expressed needs and the qualitative requirements laid down by the three services.

DRDO is working in various areas of military technology which include aeronautics, armaments, combat vehicles, electronics, instrumentation engineering systems, missiles, materials, naval systems, advanced computing, simulation and life sciences. DRDO while striving to meet the cutting edge weapons technology provides ample spin-off benefits to the society at large, thereby contributing to the nation building.

The above charter conveys the goal as design and development up to production stage, but gives no indication of how and who would be responsible (and accountable) for integrating the design produced by DRDO with the designated production agency. As seen in the earlier chapters, one of the most serious problems in aircraft design, development and production is the vertical disjunction between design, development and production agencies. China and the Soviet Union experienced similar problems till the Soviet Union clearly brought the production agencies directly under the design bureaus. For, such lack of vertical integration within government agencies controlling and managing aircraft agencies is not only inexplicable but a sure recipe of limited success in self-reliance, as indeed the experience in other countries also indicates. And, unfortunately, this has been a major factor retarding defence indigenisation in India to rectify which a number of proposals for the establishment of an Aeronautics Commission (on lines similar to those concerning space and atomic energy) have been made, including that argued for by Dr. V.S. Valluri, the former Chiefs of the Air

Staff like Air Chief Marshals O.P. Mehra, S. Krishnaswamy, etc. and the much later President of the Aeronautical Society of India. And nowhere has this problem assumed more critical proportions than in the LCA programme.

A classical example was the issue of the IAF's attempts since 1956 to standardise rocket weapons on fighter aircraft on the 68mm rocket and the Arrow pod then used by the Mystere and proposed for the HF-24. The DRDO laboratory had designed the Indian equivalent of the Arrow pod but its electronic actuator to fire the rockets could not be refined to provide the requisite reliability. Meanwhile, HAL, the production agency for the Arrow pod, had produced 1,000 pods and the IAF was forced to accept them without the actuators of the requisite quality. The ordnance factories were to have designed and produced the rockets in three versions: with practice head, HE (High Explosive) head and the API (Armour Piercing Incendiary) head. Although the programme started in 1957, till 1982, the ordnance factories had not been able to proceed beyond about 1,000 practice rockets. By that time, of course, the IAF had moved onto Soviet designed fighters which then equipped nearly 24 squadrons with MiG-21/23 and Su-7 aircraft, the bulk of them manufactured by HAL. Every single aircraft was supplied to the IAF with four 57mm rocket pods each (standard equipment on Soviet fighter aircraft launched rockets) and by 1982, there were over 5,000 rocket pods for 57mm calibre in stock, while the Director General Ordnance Factories (DGOF), on one side, and HAL and DRDO, on the other, were trying to develop 68mm rockets and pods.

The decentralisation of decision-making and the attempts to create horizontal links in an essentially vertically structured system should enable research institutes to engage in more relevant research. Chinese reforms during the 1980s, many of which had to undergo further reforms in the process of change, began to create such linkages by the end of the 1980s. While change as a consequence of the reforms remained slow in many cases, substantive and rapid change had begun to show results by the early 1990s.[20] General L. Jinai, the former head of the General Armaments Department (GAD), the lead procurement agency of the PLA stated that "there has been a marked improvement in national defence scientific research and in building of weapons and equipment. The past five years has been the best period of development in the country's history."[21]

This was the period when China started getting access to Russian military technology and the Ministry of Aerospace Industry was corporatised; and the selected technologies could be absorbed better because of a decade of reforms in the defence science and technology sectors. By the early 1990s, Chinese reforms in the defence industry had moved a long way toward greater capability and efficiency. By integrating military and civilian goods manufacture in the defence industries, China had reduced the cost of investments on the defence side being offset/subsidised by the profits from the production for the civil market. All that the Chinese defence industry lacked at that time was access to military technology which was seen as crucial in aerospace after the 1991 Gulf War. The route to technology opened up with the collapse of the Soviet Union and the economic and social chaos that followed which China used to great effect through a selective selection of high-technology systems.

To sum up, it would be useful to quote at some length from a RAND study on China's aviation/defence industry for indicators for our own future policy:[22]

Aviation industry leaders are making efforts to improve further the operations of the aviation sector by making individual enterprises responsible for their own finances and management, engaging military aircraft producers for civilian aircraft, acquiring Russian and Israeli military aircraft technology, and listing aviation firms on China's capital markets. China's aviation industry has considerable human resources and a strong institutional foundation, is upgrading its design and manufacturing capabilities, is receiving increasing financial inputs, and enjoys the 'followers advantage' of being able to acquire mature technologies at a lesser cost than the original developer. In addition, the modicum of competition that occurs at different levels in the aviation sector has created some incentives for greater efficiency and innovation in military production.

An Indian Experience

Given the summary of the Russian and Chinese experiences and their final shift from fractured research and design institutions in relation to production facilities to an integrated approach to the two sides of the same coin, we need to note that in both cases, finally, they had to set up a Ministry of Aviation to manage the aerospace industry. The demands from the late 1960s for establishing an Aeronautics Commission under a Ministry of Aeronautics to provide the necessary synergy in India failed to fructify essentially because of turf battles in South Block. While many eminent IAF senior officers served as General Managers (GM) and Chairmen HAL, the fact is that policy is made in South Block. In the absence of an overarching Aeronautics Commission to ensure an integrated approach to research, design, development and manufacture of aircraft, one must ask a simple question: who is the most affected stakeholder in the aircraft industry? The simple answer is: the Indian Air Force for military aircraft.

The example of the Indian Navy's far greater success in indigenisation of warships needs to be seen in the above context since the Indian Navy is the biggest stakeholder in warships. In fact, the Indian Navy followed the British practice where the Admiralty controlled warship design and construction, though it took the Indian Navy a few years to set up the necessary institutions. The first step was the decision in 1950 to expand the dockyards in Bombay to be able to accommodate and repair the warships for the Navy projected in the 1948 plan. Predictably, the Bombay Port Trust authorities and the Maharashtra government did not take very kindly to the dockyard expansion plans. The controversies delayed the programme by two years. Looking at the delays, Defence Minister Krishna Menon ordered dissolution of the Naval Dockyard Committee which had been overseeing the expansion of the dockyard on behalf of the Government of India and ordered the formation of the Naval Dockyard Scheme with Commodore (later Admiral and Chief of the Naval Staff) S.M. Nanda as its first Director General, with financial and administrative authority to steer the project.[23]

By 1955, Naval HQ had taken a decision to form a Corps of Naval Constructors — professional naval architects who play a pivotal role in the design and construction of warships. A contract was signed for the licensed production of the British Leander class frigates at Mazagon Docks Ltd. Six Leander class frigates were constructed which also included in-house major design changes, including the embarkation of a large helicopter instead of a small helicopter on the last two frigates. By the time the Leander class frigates construction finished, an in-house design organisation, the Directorate of Naval Design, was set up at Naval HQ as an integral part of the Navy.[24] This started the process of indigenous design and development and construction of naval warships. Old Soviet missiles were taken off some ships and installed on the INS *Talwar* (acquired from the UK). These successes led the Navy to design our own Indian frigate, the Godavari class.[25] In due course, the Navy designed and produced the Delhi class missile destroyer of over 6,500 ton displacement, the largest ship to be designed and built by that time, and launched in 1996, which had led to the Western professional media to describe it as a cruiser. Three of the Delhi class ships were built and they have been performing admirably at sea.

The Directorate of Naval Design now functions as part of the Staff Branch and its capability is recognised as a core strategic activity. A Submarine Design Group (SDG) as a full-fledged directorate under Naval HQ was also created after the HDW submarines were acquired. Most important, the design organisation is not only responsible for undertaking warship designs, but also coordinates and monitors the production of ships designed by it in what has been referred to as "womb to tomb" responsibility.[26] Inevitably, the R&D activity precedes the design process. For this purpose, in relation to weapons and systems integration, a directorate of Weapons and Electronic System Engineering Establishment (WESEE) also functions integral to, and under, the Naval HQ. The design organisation, Controller of Warship Production (CWP), and WESEE all come under the VCNS (Vice Chief of the Naval Staff) at Naval HQ.

The Navy is now building its first aircraft carrier, long termed as the Air Defence Ship (ADS). The original design studies in the mid-1980s planned for a 16,000 ton displacement vessel. But this could only take a combat aircraft like the Harrier STOVL fighter. But given the limitations of performance of the Harrier and the fact that its successor would be difficult to find, the design had to be increased to a 24,000 ton vessel in order to take a fixed-wing high performance fighter on board. However, no dockyard had the facilities to take on such a large ship. Eventually, the requisite dockyard was built at Cochin Shipyard. Naval Staff Requirements were once again revised to build an aircraft carrier of 38,000 ton displacement which would be able to embark aircraft like the MiG-29K and LCA. This clearly proves the wisdom and advantage of a strong linkage between the operational imperatives and design limitations with shipbuilding capacity — all in accordance with the operational requirements of the main stakeholder (the Indian Navy). In short, **the Navy has been able to build a strong self-reliance capability by keeping the design, development and production in a seamless synergy, with DRDO laboratories being consulted as required**. The result, as Rear Admiral Gupta wrote in 2006, was that, "More than 80 ships have been built indigenously, including over 50 to indigenous designs undertaken by the Navy in-house. This is a substantial portion of today's operational Navy."[27]

If we were to take the experience of the Russian, Chinese and Indian Navies, it is clear that if the IAF has to move more actively toward self-reliance, it must translate its stakeholding role into control and management of design and development of aircraft. There would, of course, be criticism as to why a fighting force needs to expand into design and development of aircraft. But the above three examples, which include one of the sister armed forces in India, would indicate that there is no real alternative except perhaps to go back to the concept of an Aeronautics Commission under a Department of Aeronautics (under the Prime Minister, as is the case with space and atomic energy, or under the Minister of Defence and managed by a Minister of State for Aeronautics) that could then also deal with the requirements of the fast developing civil aviation sector in India.

Some Lessons from the Past

Perhaps the most crucial lesson that we can draw from the past is that while HAL acquired great expertise and extensive experience in overhaul and production of aircraft (it built over 700 MiG-21 in two decades, to give but one example), its design and development limb had remained atrophied. When the British Indian government took over HAL in 1942, it reduced the factory to mere repair and overhaul. While this role was important for the USAAF operating in the Asia-Pacific region, there was no reason to have stopped all efforts to design and develop future aircraft. In fact, it even stopped any licensed manufacture of badly needed fighter and transport aircraft for the war in the East. If this could be explained in terms of the colonial policy described by J.R.D. Tata stating that they did want India to manufacture aircraft, the progressive and almost sustained negligence to design and develop aircraft at Asia's largest aircraft industry infrastructure is strange.

In particular, while it was logical to have brought in the German design team headed by Dr. Kurt Tank in the mid-1950s when embarking on an ambitious programme of the supersonic multi-role combat aircraft, the HF-24 Marut, it is surprising that this arrangement was not pursued so as to train a robust design and development team in HAL. A logical step was a follow-on design of an aircraft, possibly a strike aircraft like the concept of the HF-73 aircraft and retaining the German team in full or part for such a purpose. At the same time, having seen the design and qualities of the Gnat, it is surprising why the offer of Dr. Petter, the designer, to come to India and design and develop a somewhat larger fighter based on the Gnat design was not accepted. No country with a successful aircraft industry has relied on one-off designs and the successful ones (including the USA, Soviet Union and

China) have invariably engaged in multiple designs many of which actually did not go into production. In fact, the Soviet model of incremental development with minimum changes in design and systems being upgraded, provides the most cost-effective solution. Unlike other countries, design and development was accorded a low priority even in the hierarchy of decision-making which in reality was being done in South Block where, barring a few notable examples, the Secretaries of Defence Production averaged tenures of less than a year each, with most of the incumbents having little or no prior experience in the aircraft industry.

The nadir of HAL's design bureau came with the setting up of the Aeronautical Development Agency (ADA) to design the LCA as an agency outside the HAL and the Department of Defence Production, created as a registered society under the Scientific Adviser to the Defence Minister and the Secretary, Defence R&D in the Ministry of Defence. The HAL Design Bureau, incidentally, was only in the Bangalore Complex and no such facility was ever set up at the MiG Complex (spanning Nasik, Koraput and Hyderabad). In a way, the creation of ADA followed an earlier example when transport aircraft manufacture (of the Avro HS-748) under licence was set up within the IAF BRD (Base Repair Depot) which functioned and produced the first two aircraft during the first five years before being recreated as another HAL Division at Kanpur which now manufactures Dornier 228 aircraft under licence. No design and development units were set up at Kanpur either. To cap it all, the HAL behemoth never set up an engine design and development capability and this was left to GTRE (Gas Turbine Research Establishment) which developed the after-burner for the HF-24 which was successful on the test bench, but did not prove successful in actual flight — another instance of the challenges of satisfactorily productionising designed systems that work well on the test bench.

But it must be said to the credit of ADA that the LCA has been flying for almost a decade, although it entered the pipeline in the late 1970s and first flew in 1991, over two decades after the IAF laid down the operational need for an "LCA," as recorded in an earlier chapter; and by all accounts is a good combat aircraft. But its history is marked by innumerable instances of lack of coordination leave alone synergy. In essence, HAL was left out of the design and development of India's modern combat aircraft even to the extent that an ad-hoc National Test Flight Centre was formed virtually excluding the HAL test pilots! HAL's role was upturned to being a sub-contractor to ADA for the manufacture of the airframe, etc. Unfortunately, the aircraft was designed around an unknown engine, the indigenous Kaveri, designed by GTRE, and an unknown MMR (Multi-Mode Radar) for air interception with BVR (Beyond Visual Range) missiles and other capabilities.

Contrary to the IAF's view, at least in the Operations Branch, the aeronautical scientists and engineers (many of them in DRDO and/or NAL) pressed for inclusion of four new technologies, especially the Fly-By-Wire (FBW) flight controls (computer controlled) system in the aircraft. Although the opinion of the then squadron commanders was sought and they, without adequate knowledge of the complexities of aircraft design and manufacture, inevitably endorsed the scientists' proposal in the hope of getting a "state-of-the-art" combat aircraft, Air Marshal Philip Rajkumar, long associated with the LCA programme from many sides, states that "the IAF was not wanting to sound overly pessimistic, went along with these ideas, and took the first step of issuing an AST for a multi-role fighter while expressing serious reservations about the development schedule."[28] In principle, and contrary to the accepted practice worldwide, **technology (whose development had not even started in DRDO laboratories and/or HAL) was allowed to override operational imperatives for a battlefield multi-role combat aircraft that could be acquired in large numbers**. The original estimate of the IAF requirement was for the LCA to be its "work-horse" with strength of around 450 aircraft in service.

Rajkumar is not correct when he justifies that these technologies (like the glass cockpit and FBW systems, etc) were required to match the aircraft due to changes in the techno-operational environment since the LCA was to be also a low-cost aircraft and replace the MiG-21 aircraft when these would start finishing their lives by the mid-1990s. The MiG-21 had been modified successfully with the modern head-up display and inertial navigation system, etc. in the late 1970s, as a flight safety requirement; but this was not followed up. Even then, and 15 years later, both China and Pakistan, our potential adversaries, have a large inventory of the Chinese version (named F-7) of the Soviet MiG-21 inferior to even the IAF's upgraded MiG-21, especially as Rajkumar admits, "HAL had no experience of working with any of the technologies which had to be incorporated into the new aircraft to meet operational requirement targets set out in the AST. They were very underconfident of developing an aircraft by the mid-1990s to meet IAF reequipment plans."[29] I recall arguing (even in the media) that we would do well to reopen the MiG-21 manufacture line with Soviet assistance. This would have provided the cushion to build the LCA. More important, the simpler incremental approach would not have needed the large component of foreign exchange and the cost of the aircraft, as visualised by Air HQ in the early 1980s would been far more affordable. But the inevitable lure of the "silver bullet" kept pushing the LCA toward a complex high-technology design. In 1986, the government sanctioned the manufacture of five prototypes at a cost of Rs. 575 crore.

Another mistake was to follow the DRDO's taking on the role of high-technology aircraft and jet engines *design and development* with the choice of consultants and foreign partners for the most crucial part of the new technologies, the FBW flight control system. By end 1988, the Project Definition Phase (PDP) was completed by ADA and the report was circulated to various agencies. Air HQ, after going through the report, expressed its reservations about ADA's ability to design the aircraft to meet the AST and assessed that the time indicated for design and development for induction was far too ambitious. The IAF recommended that a confidence and competence building route of proving the four crucial technologies by flying "two technology demonstrator aircraft" be followed before embarking on full-scale engineering development of prototypes. In effect, this detached the Indian Air Force from the project in spite of being the primary stakeholder.

Dassault Aviation of France was very keen to partner ADA in the LCA programme and offered the three digital channels with an analogue fourth channel FBW technology which they had successfully developed for the Rafale. But for reasons difficult to explain, the offer was rejected in favour of the American offer of the quadruplex digital FBW technology. Consequently, the French walked out of the project. As could be anticipated at any time, there was always the risk of the US imposing its technology denial regimes and sanctions. In fact, India was under sanctions since 1978; and fresh sanctions and imposition of the technology denial regime that finally happened more than once to delay the LCA programme.

Rajkumar believes that this decision and its follow-on decisions to go in for only consultancy agreements with foreign entities added a decade to the programme. He says:[30]

> This decision, I suspect, was taken *because the thrust was to acquire the latest technology and build self-reliance through indigenisation rather than on delivery of an operational fighter in a reasonable time-frame to meet IAF modernisation plans.* It was a classic case of the 'best' being the enemy of the 'good.' Operational requirements should drive technology choices and not the other way around. (Emphasis added.)

The LCA is flying and flying well. But since it had to rely on only two prototypes for testing for many years, the overall testing period has been elongated. But now it seems that the aircraft weight is significantly higher than what the design defined. This problem seems to have dogged HAL for decades, on most of the aircraft it produced. Hence, the aircraft reportedly falls short of critical parameters of performance like the rate of turn, etc. with the GE-404 engine acquired from the United States in 1987. I remember many discussions with Dr. V.S. Arunachalam, Scientific Adviser to the Defence Minister and also head of the ADA, in the late 1980s, about the likely problem in this area because there was always a risk that the Kaveri engine may not come up to expectation in time. Design and development of jet engines with high thrust and reliability for a single-engine modern fighter is not an easy process. This is also the reason why there are only a few firms in the world that manufacture such high performance engines. The US had decided after the end of the Cold War that at least two major engine manufacturers must be kept in business because it was too risky to rely on one. Dr Arunachalam, while agreeing with me that the problems of the HF-24 essentially rested in our failure to power it with a suitable engine, used to assure me that they had taken this factor into account and at least five different engines (including the MiG-29 engine) from four countries could be fitted to the LCA. But perhaps the ADA had not considered the possibility of the aircraft weight increasing significantly. This problem can now be resolved only through fitting a more powerful engine which may require airframe modifications and more testing, stretching the time-frame further; RFPs have been issued for a more powerful engine and selection would take some time. Hence, the IAF, now critically short of combat aircraft, has placed an order for 20 aircraft of limited performance to be followed by another 20 once the first squadron is formed.

We also need to note that in spite of a close relationship with the Soviet Union and Russia for more than half a century and building more than a thousand Soviet designed aircraft in HAL factories, we did not seek to establish a joint venture in aircraft design and development till very recently. It can be argued that this is beginning to happen now with the plans to design the fifth generation fighter and the medium transport aircraft. Obviously, this can be seen as the experience of the ADA over the past quarter century where its establishment was a serious blow to HAL's credibility as an aircraft industry. No doubt, that it got going more realistically to design and develop the IJT (Intermediate Jet Trainer), the aircraft that would start replacing the HJT-16 in a few years.

THE WAY AHEAD

... it will be good if the time-tested model of aeronautical development followed in the Western world is adopted. In that environment, new technologies are developed by the R&D agencies, the aeronautical industry designs and develops the aircraft and the uniformed user service manages the project. Ad hoc programme management offices should not be created.

— Air Marshal Philip Rajkumar[31]

India has come a long way since the colonial deindustrialisation. But it would be naïve to ignore the fact that the broad base of technological and industrial capacity — or, for that matter, the intellectual capacity — has been acquired to support the country as a growing major power. The growth of industrial capacity has inevitably been slow since the country simply had no capital (the Gross Saving Rate was around 6 percent in 1950), no market, negligible industry and in spite of being an agrarian civilisation, it could not feed itself for two decades after independence. The priorities of the government were naturally far more focussed on elimination of poverty (with nearly 85 percent of the population living below the poverty line). But contrary to conventional wisdom, defence was not ignored, including the raising of defence industry from a few workshops to a modern industrial sector. Overall, it is obvious that compressing the Industrial Revolution in India into a few decades cannot equal the fruits of the Industrial Revolution over three decades in the developed countries, for most of the time at the cost paid by the developing (the colonies of recent decades) countries. It is to understand this that the first chapter was written to provide the background in a somewhat longer context. To this has to be added the major and recurrent problem of acute shortage of hard currency and foreign exchange till the last decade.

Things are happening in India in every segment and at a faster rate during the first decade of the 21st century, so much so that one can assume that India has arrived on the world stage although much hard work needs to be done. In terms of its needs for military arms, and equipment, it stands out as the world's largest market. Given that the country has been one of the two fastest growing economies, it would be easy to carry on business as usual: buy some from abroad, and build some under licence, in keeping with what we have been doing for the past half century. But, obviously, India cannot grow into a major power unless it can achieve the maximum degree of independence in its arms and military technology. Most of the issues that need addressing can be found in the previous chapters. Here, in the final chapter, the best we can do is to point out toward the way we should be taking, with major sign posts that require in our judgement to be addressed, and hope that democratic professional debates and discussions would lead to specific building of capabilities, including the intellectual capacities.

Aviation Industrial Policy[32]
In spite of extensive search and study, we have not been able to find a document that indicates, leave alone comprehensively spells out, the aviation industry policy of the government. There are, of course, the Industrial Policy resolutions of 1948 and 1958; and there other statements here and there. There is an elaborate DPP (Defence Procurement Procedure) in recent years which has been modified almost every year. But this spells out the procedure which is not the same thing as policy! This is why the question arises: why was it found necessary to establish the ADA (on HAL land) when HAL existed with an enormous aviation industry infrastructure next only to that of China amongst the developing world?

And having set up the ADA more than a quarter century ago, what was the overriding rationale of NAL under the CSIR under the Ministry of Science and Technology designing aircraft like the Hansa trainer and Saras light transport aircraft which would have to be built at HAL? This, curiously, was not very different from DGCA, the aviation regulatory body which decided to design a trainer in collaboration with IIT, Delhi, in the process, the IAF's requirement for a new primary trainer being held up by HAL (on instructions from South Block) for almost a decade. It appears that there has been a keenness to take on tasks by agencies which rightly should have fallen within the ambit of some other organisation and institution. NAL's contribution to the development of technologies has been highly commendable. It had already developed the composite technology that was to form the basis of the LCA design and, hence, could be transferred to ADA and HAL. The latter would need a larger autoclave for the wing structures of the LCA and NAL successfully built that and supplied it to HAL. One of the major reasons for the long time taken in the design and development of the LCA was the problem of getting a suitable FBW system. By the mid-1980s, the ADE (Aeronautical Development Establishment) of the Defence Ministry's DRDO had not even begun to think about such technologies which were mature enough to be installed on aircraft like the Mirage-2000 that we ordered from France in 1982! Many more examples of ad-hocism can be cited, not the least of them being the ADA which was tasked to design the LCA a quarter century ago.

But weapon designs (and defence industrial policy) normally should follow the doctrine and strategy of defence. Here, we run into another disconnect. During the years the LCA was conceived, the Indian government had not defined a clear national defence doctrine and strategy in spite of severe critique from the Estimates Committee of the Parliament which had stated:[33]

> Further, the Committee deprecate the fact that the country has fought four wars and launched armed operations in and at the request of neighbouring countries without a clear articulated and integrated defence policy. The Committee firmly believe that underlying the question of force levels is the question of having a formal National Security Doctrine. The Committee are deeply disturbed at the absence of such a doctrine.

Under the title of Inadequacy of Existing Force Levels, the committee were also informed, "Air Headquarters are examining the need and possibility of establishing a Strategic Command with control over all strategic forces and means, including strategic reconnaissance, airlift, long range strike and surface-to-surface engagement. In this context, the Committee are acutely conscious of the fact that, as has been conclusively demonstrated during the recently fought Gulf War, in future the country will face greater threats from the sea and the air. *The Committee are convinced that the time has come to pay far greater attention to strengthening the country's Naval and Air Power.*"[34] (Emphasis added.) In 1994, the Prime Minister (as Defence Minister) did spell out to the Parliament what he stated was "Guidelines" for the armed forces where "low intensity conflict" was raised to a second level task from being a contingency requirement for aid to civil authority.

Even in the case of the IAF, the official doctrine of the Air Force was issued only in 1995, a good 15 years after the operational need for an LCA was spelt out and over 60 years after the Air Force was established. On the other hand, the Operations Branch of the IAF had clearly indicated the parameters that it felt were necessary for the operational utilisation of the LCA in the next ten years as a replacement for the MiG-21, and, hence, was to be treated as the doctrine and strategy for the low-end of capability in the force structure for battlefield air support to the army and air superiority over the battlefield in the coming years. These, as may be seen from the foregoing narrative, were sacrificed on the altar of development of science and technology for its own sake, without reference to the IAF and reservations on the Project Definition Phase (PDP) expressed by the IAF which was then handled by rescheduling the project as a "technology demonstrator."

Even in this case, unfortunately, the original parameters were lost and the end result has been a massive drop in IAF combat force level from 39.5 squadrons to around 28 squadrons, creating a window of vulnerability that may take 10-15 years to deal with successfully. It is ironic that what was visualised in 1980 as the LCA has been more or less reproduced by China in collaboration with Pakistan and help from Russia in the shape of the JF-17 (Thunder in Pakistan, and FC-1 Fierce Dragon in China) in less than a decade and the PAF has already ordered 250 aircraft!

Institutional Structures and Reforms

Serious thought needs to be given to the need and direction of institutional reforms which actually should have been undertaken in or soon after early 1991 when the economy was liberalised. As we have seen, both Russia and China went through a long period of reforms in the defence industry sector and came to the conclusion that the three aspects of design and development, technological R&D and manufacture of weapons need to be seamlessly integrated. Russia had put the designers as the main drivers of the industry, whereas the Chinese have followed a more complex system which shows in the deficit in the design area though they have developed many aircraft by copying the Russian designs, the J-11 (as a copy of the Russian Sukhoi Su-27) being the latest example.

The most important issue facing us, as our study above shows, is the issue of design, development and manufacture of aircraft and the organisational system under which it should be undertaken. In principle, this should rest on the framework identified by Major General B.D. Kapur, the first head (as CCR&D) of defence research and development in the mid-1950s, when he wrote:[35]

The direction of research was the business of the scientists, but the
direction of weapon design and development should be with (military)
service heads for coordination and management.

This is along the lines that Air Marshal Philip Rajkumar
formulates the institutional structures for the future, as noted at
the beginning of the section above. General Kapur's argument
was that this approach would telescope the time period from
the creation of an idea to the production of a prototype.
He had also argued that (i) senior scientists should have no
administrative responsibility and should apply their minds
solely to the tasks assigned to them and information should be
passed on to them; and (ii) for defence science to be effective,
it should be shorn of bureaucratic delays and, therefore, the
organisation should have complete autonomy.[36]

Here **the Indian naval model of design, development
and manufacture of warships where the Naval HQ contains
a Directorate of Naval Design and also the WESEE for
system development and integration in the warship, besides
the Controller of Warship Production, is highly worthy of
emulation by the IAF.** The system, based on the British
Admiralty system, has proven itself over the past six decades
to be highly successful. While the Indian Navy, no doubt, has
many problems, glitches and handicaps to resolve on the
way to making this integrated approach, it has succeeded in
producing outstanding warships like the Delhi class and other
warships. Overall, one also must concede that while it has also
relied on DRDO and the dockyards, there has been much
less acrimony between the Service and DRDO/dockyards as
compared to the Indian Army's (a la Arjun MBT, etc.) and the
IAF's (HF-24, Gnat/Ajeet/LCA, and HPT-32, etc.) problems
which have led to serious erosion of mutual faith and trust — a
factor that is crucial, especially in the aircraft industry. In fact,

Air Chief Marshal P.C. Lal, soon after taking over as the CAS in 1969, had carried out changes in Air HQ where a separate Director of Projects had been set up under the ACAS (Plans) as distinct from the DASR (Director Air Staff Requirements). Unfortunately, it never functioned according to his vision because the remaining blocks of the defence industry system were moving in different directions. Later, in 1980, the IAF undertook a system integration of sub-systems to create a new navigation and weapon aiming system named DARIN for the Jaguar in-house [under the IIO (Inertial-navigation Integration Organisation)] which made the IAF Jaguars far superior to the British and French ones.

This system can be implemented now by the simple method of appointing the Director General of ADA under the Chief of the Air Staff as an additional Deputy Chief of the Air Staff and merge the HAL's design bureaus, what little exists, with the ADA. The IAF has the deepest stake in the aviation industry compared to any other interest group since finally its air warriors and aircrew in particular are the real combatants who also bear the risks during peace-time of any failures and accidents. Every pilot in the Air Force knows very well that not only his performance, but even his life, depends upon the professionalism of his colleagues, the professional competence of the technicians and the quality of the aircraft design and maintenance. The last has been outside the control of the Air Force. For example, as noted earlier, the Gnat had an accident rate nearly nine times that of the HF-24. The Gnat was an excellent aircraft, but it also cost the Air Force an enormously high price. It would be difficult to find an Air Officer who has not attended the funeral of a colleague, friend and compatriot. This creates a bond which is unique to the Air Force.

The other alternative would be to transfer ADA to HAL (or vice versa) to build a larger design bureau for the future, eliminating the need for the DG DRDO to remain as the Chairman of the ADA society. One needs to accept that design activity is an almost continuous process, especially when we note the size of the Air Force required for future commitments and the air power requirements of the Indian Army and Indian Navy. As far back as 1991-92, when I was invited by the Scientific Adviser to the Defence Minister to attend the review committee of HAL chaired by Defence Minister Sharad Pawar, I had argued that given the success in certain technology developments, ADA should seriously consider launching a follow-on programme so that the gap between one design effort and the next does not become too large (as, indeed, had happened between the HF-24 and the LCA). HAL itself needs to undergo significant reforms which in principle should lead to corporatisation and, at the same time, make the different divisions far more autonomous, bordering on independence, with their own Board of Directors. A strengthened Design Division with the requisite powers would need to be brought under the IAF as the primary stakeholder.

The third option is the old proposal: to establish an Aeronautics Commission under a Department of Aeronautics preferably under the PM's office like the Space and Atomic Energy Departments.

Indigenisation Strategy

The change in the world situation has produced new challenges as well as new opportunities. One of these opportunities is the more relaxed relationship with the United States and its allies which can make it possible to acquire arms and military technology from Western sources. Our own economic growth at an average of over 8 percent during the past decade and foreign exchange reserves in the order of around US$ 290 billion (far less than what China has) provide the necessary means to reshape our indigenisation strategy. Given the reality of deep gaps in IAF inventories, leave alone the need to induct new technology systems, this would require large sums. But, more important, this would require sound policies.

One of the crucial methods in these policies is the issue of offsets which gained strength after the collapse of the Soviet Union and the end of the Cold War. Most arms transfers after that began to include offsets in the terms of sales and some of the offsets were in the order of as much as 150 percent and more of the value of the arms contract.[37] The study highlighted that "as much as 82 percent of US arms sales abroad include offsets; and 80-90 percent of global offsets are concentrated in the aerospace sector, primarily because of the high costs involved." It may be useful to note some definitions of the term offsets to grasp its full dimensions. In 1986, a US inter-agency group defined offsets as "industrial compensation practices required as a condition of purchase in either governmental sales of defence articles and/or defence services as specified in the International Traffic in Arms Regulations."[38] Offsets arrangements commit the seller country/firm to provide technology, purchase locally produced components, or provide other forms of assistance to the buyer country that go beyond compensation economically necessary to support the sale.[39] Obviously, the implementation of offsets can take many shapes. Our study showed that importing countries have generally mandated offsets requirement by law, often to 100 percent of the arms contract value. The exporting countries also hope to take advantage of offsets to expand their production runs through economies of scale in a globally declining arms market where arms sales are much more a buyers market. In short, "An offsets regime would help to build interdependence and create stakeholders, especially if we are able to access American arms directly."[40]

Since then, South Block has moved to introduce the offsets clause in all defence acquisitions of a value of more than $300 million to the extent of 30 percent of the value of the contract. However, this is still a major issue that is not adequately understood in South Block in spite of the creation of a dedicated agency, the Defence Offsets Authority, under a Joint Secretary in the Department of Defence Production. It may be recalled that our study had concluded in 2004 that, "In view of the specialised nature of the task of leveraging an offsets strategy for national security, it may be advisable (or perhaps, inescapable) for the government to set up a standing National Task Force for Offsets under the Prime Minister's chief adviser for science and technology."[41]

It is in the foregoing context that we need to look at some of the arms sales processes now going on, in which the requirement of 126 (likely to increase to 200) MMRCA (Medium Multi-Role Combat Aircraft) occupies an important position for a variety of reasons. The Air Force has completed its evaluation of all the six contenders and the ball is now with South Block, at both its defence and external affairs wings. The fact that the estimated US$ 10 billion contract would bring in half of this sum back in India for investments is important, but not a crucial factor in the further moves to select the fighter since it is common to all of them. What is critical to my mind is the type, extent and method of bringing in technologies to India. All weapon systems of this type now have a design life closer to

30-40 years (compared to 10-15 years earlier). The aircraft and its systems are already designed, with almost entirely proven technologies. Hence, we can only get production technology with the contract to manufacture the aircraft in India. But there is an option and necessity to go beyond that.

The life of the airframe and most systems may be 30-40 years, but technologically, the aircraft will require upgrades within the first 10-15 years in systems and sub-systems. Hence, the need for the OEM (Original Equipment Manufacturer) to establish appropriate R&D facilities, preferably in collaboration with the private sector to manufacture the sub-systems with an eye on what upgrades would be needed which could be developed in these facilities. The principle would be that the first upgrade should be carried out with significant Indian involvement to enable us to move toward undertaking the second upgrade, another 10-odd years later, all on our own. That is the only way the fighter after the MMRCA could be designed in India, if need be in partnership with a foreign company to enlarge the economics of scale and not because we will be dependent on foreign sources for technology.

Conclusion

Indian manufacturing output and its national income had constituted a quarter of the global output in the mid-18th century. It was the wealth of India that attracted foreign invaders. But till the British arrived in the late 16th century, the invaders came from the northwest via the land route, passing through choke points of just two narrow passes — the Khyber Pass west of Peshawar, and the Bolan Pass north of Quetta further south which the rulers mostly chose not to defend, waiting instead to fight defensively at Panipat (under what may be termed as the "Panipat Syndrome"), losing the strategic advantage of forward defence at the difficult to transit through narrow passes of the Hindu Kush ranges. These invaders either looted the current wealth and went back like Mohammad Ghauri, or simply stayed back, becoming part of the Indian culture and civilisation and, in turn, enriching Indian culture by their own from Central Asia, like the Mughals. But the British intrusion into India was patently different. Firstly, they came via the sea, initially to trade with this rich country, using the sea route all the way back to Europe. It is often forgotten that it was a trading company — the East India Company — that ruled India for the first 150-odd years while it expanded its rule progressively all the way from Bombay to Calcutta and then north to the Yamuna river, concurrently expanding from Karachi through Sindh to what later came to be termed as the NWFP (Northwest Frontier Province), a nomenclature that the Company had adopted for the northwest frontiers of its rule earlier. But what became even more crucial was the historical convergence of two factors that changed Indian history and, more relevant to the current study, the nature of Indian economic means of productivity and, hence, its industrial capabilities, in turn, leading to its impoverishment.

By the time the British traders were seeking a licence to trade in India, the Industrial Revolution was beginning to take root in England and by the middle of the 18th century, it had not only reached a fairly advanced stage, but the British and Europeans had evolved technologically far superior arms manufactured in their factories in large numbers. This, in turn, started the interconnected process of history by its sheer coincidence: superior military technology enabled it to defeat any and every military force on the subcontinent, and the superior military power that the trading company established allowed it to be an arbiter in political and military terms among the local rulers, inheritors of the disintegrating Mughal Empire already weakened by the erosion of the central Mughal rule since Aurangzeb. Progressive colonisation of India since the early 18th century (when the East India Company had to take permission from Indians to hire guards for their "factories" in Bombay) led to an inevitable process of deindustrialisation of India during the two centuries since the Industrial Revolution had started. During this period, military technology advanced dramatically and the earlier Indian weapons and arms became obsolete and almost useless in this process. Although India provided enormous resources, including manpower, to fight Britain's wars including World Wars I and II (India providing 2.6 million men under arms in the latter case, making it the largest volunteer military force to have ever fought in history), the British took care not to establish any arms production capacity in India, leave alone any military technology transfer. Even the weapons with which the Indian Army, Navy and Air Force were equipped in World War II were, as a matter of imperial policy, inferior to those of the British troops in India. By the time the British left this country in 1947, India's share of global manufacturing output and national income had dropped from 25 percent in the early 18th century to a little over half a percent in spite of the fact that Britain required arms and equipment production in India to equip even its own forces after the Japanese invaded Southeast Asia and ultimately tried to advance into India through the Indo-Burma border.

It is not intended to go into the details of the changes that took place as a consequence of the colonisation of India. Suffice it to say here that at its independence, India inherited extremes of poverty, a deindustrialised nation deficient in food, where a couple of years before independence the Great Bengal Famine had led to more than one percent of the country's population dying of hunger. An aircraft factory set up in 1940 by the initiative of a private businessman in collaboration with a private aircraft manufacturer from the United States had already manufactured a trainer aircraft and was in the process of designing a fighter aircraft. But when the war spread to Southeast Asia in 1942, this was taken over the British Indian government. However, in spite of the tremendous shortage of aircraft in India, the government, instead of furthering the Indo-American cooperation across the full range of aircraft manufacture, design and development — or at least production of British fighters under licence in India (while Britain was acquiring arms from America on a lend-lease basis in any case) — took over control of the factory and regressed its development by assigning the role of overhaul to it, stopping the process of design and development of aircraft. The handful of workshops in the country that existed at that time were tasked to produce rifles and ammunition besides mortars.

It is in this background that we need to see the economic, technological and political difficulties in creating a viable defence industry after independence. The most difficult challenge that the country faced during the six decades since independence has been access to military technology which has always been retained and often used as an instrument of foreign policy by the developed countries (almost all of them being former imperial/colonial powers). Till recently, barriers to access to even civilian technology, leave alone military technology, had simply kept going up for one reason or the other. Only the Soviet Union was willing to make allowances to India because of the great advantage it perceived for its own interests in the process. But here we did not seek technology for design and development and were more than happy with technology for defence production of Soviet designed weapons and equipment. This was useful in the sense that it did provide a degree of self-reliance. But it also encouraged a sense of complacency which led to the erosion and even decline of design and development of weapon systems. The Ordnance Factory Board (which manages 9 factories and supplies munitions (mostly to the Army) worth over Rs. 14,000 crore every year does not even have a design bureau! The design bureaus in other segments of defence industry, especially HAL, established in the beginning, had become non-entities in most cases till the beginning of the 21st century. However, it would take a long time for the design and development capabilities to come up to an acceptable level. In this context, we can identify three strategic opportunities: two in the past that we have missed, and one that exists today where we are not certain if this would be exploited or not in the short-term future that such opportunities inevitably present.

Soon after independence, the government adopted a policy to achieve self-reliance in defence and, at the same time, meet perceived threats (seen as emanating only from Pakistan which was also expected to be managed through diplomacy) through a three-pronged military-technology strategy: to (i) develop design and development capacity in the country, if necessary in collaboration with the developed countries; (ii) licensed production of weapons and equipment in our own factories; and (iii) import of high technology weapons in smaller affordable quantities within the limits of foreign exchange and financial resource affordability. This is how the design of the HT-2 trainer and then of the HF-24 Marut multi-role combat aircraft (under a design meet led by the German designer Kurt Tank) were initiated; and the manufacture of the Vijayanta tank, Shaktiman and Nissan trucks, Leander class frigate, etc. was undertaken. After the 1962 Sino-Indian War and the Soviet

willingness to allow licensed production of any system that New
Delhi wanted, indigenous design and development in HAL
began to take a back seat. Political leaders talked confidently
after every contract to import weapons that this would also
be accompanied by technology transfer. The obvious mistake
has been that they mean technology transfer for production
and not for design and development since the weapon system
being acquired would already have been designed. The Soviet
source of supplies, however, did contribute to a degree of self-
reliance because of local manufacture though not of all the
systems, components and spares.

The second opportunity to make a strategic advance
in giving a major push to technology acquisition for design
and development was when the Soviet Union disintegrated.
Its defence industry was extensive and a major source for
employment of high quality professionals. Its design bureaus
were unique and of very high quality. The Soviet elites were
keen to link up design and development with India (which
would not pose any security challenge, unlike China or the
US) in joint ventures to ensure employment for the designers
and engineers. However, the Indian scientific and military
community showed no interest (after Dr Arunachalam, the
then Scientific Adviser to the Defence Minister, who saw
the opportunities that needed to be exploited, left) though
interest was fairly strong at the highest political levels. The
result was that a large number of Soviet/Russian designers left
Russia for China, the US and Israel. It was only later, toward the
end of the 1990s, that some joint ventures (like the Brahmos
cruise missile and fifth generation fighter programmes) were
initiated. But our dependence on foreign imported weapons
and equipment six decades after independence remains
inordinately high which points to fundamental weaknesses of

policy over a long time. For example, HAL took thirty years to design a combat aircraft between the HF-24 Marut (started in 1956) and the LCA Tejas in 1987! The upgrades and minor design changes to the Gnat attempted in the 1970s proved to be failures.

The third opportunity is looking into our eyes. This is the process of a major arms acquisition programme that India is embarked on to make up for the enormous backlog and deficiencies in modernisation of the weapons and equipment of its armed forces. By all accounts, India is set to invest over $100 billion in arms acquisitions over the next ten years. Visualising this situation in 2002, the Centre for Air Power Studies had started studies on defence modernisation in general and offsets as one of the key measures for access to military technology for future design and development. A series of international conferences were held to sensitise the government agencies, foreign and Indian industry and the armed forces on ways and means of energising the aerospace industry. Defence offsets were identified as a major mechanism for technology access emerging out of the arms acquisition processes.

The government was already getting ready for reforms in the arms acquisition processes and structures consequent to the Group of Ministers' Report 2001 on the management of national security. A formal Defence Offsets Procedure was adopted in 2005 and incorporated in DPP 2005 (Defence Procurement Procedure 2005). In view of the complexities of the processes involved, this has been amended and new procedures issued almost every year since then. Defence offsets are likely to result in positive benefits for an arms importing country, provided the policy orientation has a long-term direction, with clear aims, coupled with vision. The Indian defence offsets procedure has faced certain teething troubles (it still does). In order to streamline the procedure, the policy was fine-tuned in 2006 and 2008. However, it is premature to gauge the benefits of the offsets policy, as it would take a decade or two to verify the exact nature of the intended benefits. Meanwhile, the much awaited mega deal on the MMRCA is going to be a major litmus test as the offsets benefits from this deal are expected to be to the tune of around $ 5 billion, with a 50 percent offsets tag attached to it.

Increased private sector participation in defence production has been witnessed for the past five years or so in India. There is a lot of anticipation on the benefits emanating out of defence offsets. However, the government needs to do more than what has already been attempted to encourage private sector participation. For example, there is a need to encourage Foreign Direct Investment (FDI) in the defence sector by enhancing the cap from 26 percent as at present to at least 49 percent as recommended by the industry. HAL urgently needs reforms, and to be made more competitive. The quality of offsets is more important than the quantitative percentage of offsets. Incentives in the form of multipliers need to be given to those offsets which have the capability to advance the domestic defence industrial base of the country. For example, technology transfer needs to be accorded higher multipliers than say, mere export of defence hardware.

But more important, there is a crucial need to involve the primary stakeholder in aircraft industry, the *Indian Air Force*. This can best be achieved by adopting the model in force in the Indian Navy for decades which has its warship Design Division in the Naval HQ under the Vice Chief of Staff and the dockyards manufacturing warships are monitored by the Controller of Warship Construction in Naval HQ. No doubt, HAL was headed by IAF officers for at least half of its life.

But the problem is not simply with HAL, but the stake that various agencies perceive in aircraft design, development and manufacture. Any shortfall or time overruns affect the IAF in its operational capability and, hence, on India's defence preparedness and deterrence, both nuclear and conventional. The Air Force leadership needs to recognise that it is not simply a question of buying aircraft, but of having a high degree of control on aircraft design and through that, their production. If this had been adopted earlier, it is debatable if the LCA design would have flown out of control. Even when the PDP was not acceptable in 1988, instead of withdrawing from the design and development process, the Air Force could have changed the AST preferably back to the original concept of 1980 and proceeded to modify the MiG-21 to the visualised LCA standard and started a new design of the type sought in the LCA PDP.

Notes

1. S.R. Valluri, *Events in My Life: Struggle for Self-Reliance in Aeronautics* (Bangalore: Privately published, 2007), pp. 29-30.

2. Major General B.D. Kapur, independent India's first head of defence research organisation as CCR&D in the Ministry of Defence, in *Building Defence Technology Base* (New Delhi: Lancer International, 1990), p. 63.

3. Robin Higham, John T. Greenwood and Van Hardesty, eds., *Russian Aviation and Air Power in the Twentieth Century* (London: Frank Cass, 1998), pp. 132-144.

4. Ibid., p. 134.

5. This is how aircraft came to be known as the MiG (Mikoyan and Guruvich) series of fighters, the Sukhoi fighter was named after the An series for transport aircraft (designed by Antonov), Tupolev designer produced the Tu bomber/transport aircraft series, Yak, Be, etc.

6. John T. Greenwood, "The Aviation Industry, 1917-97" in Higham, et. al., eds., n. 3, p. 140.

7. The ministry served the purpose of coordinating various agencies and specialisations in producing integrated outputs in terms of the aviation

industry, what in India was sought by creating an Aeronautics Commission under a Department of Aeronautics, the model for which exists in the Atomic Energy Commission and the Space Commission which have produced remarkable results.

8. Ulrich Albright, *The Soviet Armament Industry* (Switzerland: Harvard Academic, 1993), p. 41.

9. Higham, et al, eds., n. 3, p. 146.

10. Richard E. Stockwell, "Soviet Aircraft Production" in Asher Lee, ed., *The Soviet Air and Rocket Forces* (London: Weidenfield and Nicolson, 1959), p. 246.

11. Ibid., p. 141.

12. For details about the key designers and their OKBs, see John T. Greenwood, "The Designers: Their Design Bureaux and Aircraft" in Higham, et. al., eds., n. 3, pp. 162-190.

13. Stockwell, n. 11, p. 152.

14. Merle Goldman and Denis Fred Simon, "Introduction" in Denis Fred Simon and Merle Goldman, eds., *Science and Technology in Post-Mao China* (Cambridge Mass: Harvard University Press, 1989), p. 8.

15. Tony Saich, "Reform of China's Science and Technology Organisational System" in Fred and Goldman, eds., Ibid., p. 255.

16. Tony Saich, "Reform of China's Science and Technology Organisational System" in Fred and Goldman, eds., Ibid., p. 71.

17. Ibid., p. 72.

18. Ibid., p. 78.

19. Government of India, DRDO, at http://drdo.gov.in/drdo/English/index.jsp?pg=homebody.jsp accessed on October 30, 2010.

20. Evan S. Medeiros, Roger Cliff, et. al., *A New Direction for China's Defence Industry* (Santa Monica: RAND, 2005), p. 2.

21. Ibid., p. 2.

22. "China's Military-Aviation Industry" in Ibid., p. 155.

23. Rear Admiral Satyindra Singh, *Blueprint to Bluewater: The Indian Navy 1951-65* (New Delhi: Lancer International, 1992), p. 268.

24. Rear Admiral N.P. Gupta, "Made in India," *Force* (New Delhi), February 2006, pp. 44-47.

25. Ibid., p. 44.

26. Ibid., p. 46.

27. Ibid., p. 46.

28. Air Marshal Philip Rajkumar (Retd.), *The Tejas Story: The Light Combat Aircraft Project* (New Delhi: Manohar Publishers, 2008), p. 28

29. Ibid., p. 28-29. HAL was right. With full support to the LCA programme, it is around two decades behind its original schedule laid down in the AST and the result is that the IAF is short by 25 percent of its combat force because of lack of suitable aircraft, waiting as it did for the LCA and, hence, opening up a 10-15 year window of vulnerability that, if required, will demand sacrifices from the Air Force aircrew!

30. Rajkumar, n. 28, p. 33.

31. Ibid., p. 165.

32. We will be using the term 'aviation industry' from here onward, since 'aircraft industry' is only one part of the total aviation sector.

33. Nineteenth Report of the Estimates Committee 1992-93 (Tenth Lok Sabha), Ministry of Defence, *Defence Force Levels, Manpower, Management and Policy* (New Delhi: Lok Sabha Secretariat, 1992), p. 27.

34. Ibid., p. 28-29.

35. Kapur, n. 2, p. 118.

36. Ibid., p. 118.

37. For an early study on the subject carried out in 2004, see Jasjit Singh, "Arms Trade Offsets: The Key Energise our Defence Industry," *Air Power Journal*, Vol. 2, No. 1, Spring 2005 (Jan-Mar), pp. 149-177.

38. Department of Commerce, *Offsets in Defence Trade: Third Annual Report to the Congress*, Washington DC, US Department of Commerce, August 1998, p. 1.

39. David C. Mowery, "Offsets in Commercial and Military Aerospace: An Overview," Symposium Papers on Trends and Challenges in Aerospace Offsets, January 1998, cited in *Foreign Offsets Demands in Defence and Civil Aerospace Transactions*, Minority Staff Report, Committee on Government Reform and Oversight, US House of Representatives, October 23, 1998, p. 1.

40. Singh, n. 37, p. 175.

41. Ibid., p. 177.

Author's Profile

Air Commodore **JASJIT SINGH**, AVSM, VrC, VM (Retd), born in 1934, was awarded the Padma Bhushan for a lifetime's contribution to national defence and strategic affairs, and served with great distinction in the Indian Air Force for 34 years as a fighter pilot in peace and war where he commanded a combat squadron, and was the Director of Operations. He was decorated by the President with the AVSM (Ati Vasisht Seva Medal, for distinguished service of a very high order), VrC (Vir Chakra, for gallantry in the face of the enemy), and VM (Vayu Sena Medal, for exceptional service to the Indian Air Force). He headed India's premier think-tank, the Institute for Defence Studies and Analyses (IDSA) for 14 years during the turbulent period of 1987-2001. He is the Founder Director of the Centre for Air Power Studies since 2001, an independent think-tank in New Delhi.

Jasjit Singh was appointed to a three-member Task Force to set up the National Security Council in 1998, served as a Member of the National Security Advisory Board, Adviser to the 11th Finance Commission, Member of the Planning Commission's Committee on "Vision 2020," and Member of the Governing Council of the Indian Council on World Affairs. He has been a Member of the International Pugwash Council, International Commission for a New Asia (1992-1994), International Commission for Peace and Food, Fellow of the Aeronautical Society of India, and Fellow of the World Academy

of Art and Science among numerous other institutions. He
has lectured extensively at defence and war colleges in India
and abroad (including the USA, China, USSR, Japan, NATO,
and numerous other countries). He was invited to address the
UN at its 2nd Special Session on Disarmament in June 1988.

Jasjit Singh did his Masters in History from Mysore
University and is a graduate from the Defence Services Staff
College, Wellington. He was a qualified 'A' category Flying
Instructor and Chief Flying Instructor at the Flying Instructors
School. He has published a number of books, including *Air
Power in Modern Warfare* (1985), *AWACS, the New De-stabiliser*
(1987), *India's Defence Spending* (2000), *Nuclear Defence and
Diplomacy* (jointly with Manpreet Sethi, 2004), *Defence from
the Skies* (2007) and *The Icon: Marshal of the Indian Air Force,
Arjan Singh, DFC,* besides nearly three dozen edited books.
His articles have been published extensively in newspapers,
periodicals and books in India and abroad.

Email: jasjit1934@yahoo.com

Index